WIN AT CHESS

(FORMERLY TITLED "CHESS QUIZ")

FRED REINFELD

DOVER PUBLICATIONS, INC., NEW YORK

Published in Canada by General Publishing Company, Ltd., 30 Lesmill Road, Don Mills, Toronto, Ontario.
Published in the United Kingdom by Constable and Company, Ltd., 10 Orange Street, London WC 2.

This Dover edition, first published in 1958, is an unabridged and unaltered republication of the work originally published by David McKay Company in 1945 under the title *Chess Quiz*.

International Standard Book Number: 0-486-20438-3
Library of Congress Catalog Card Number: 57-14882

Manufactured in the United States of America
Dover Publications, Inc.
180 Varick Street
New York, N. Y. 10014

INTRODUCTION

In writing this book I have made use of the guiding idea which underlies my *Chess Mastery by Question and Answer* and *Chess For Amateurs*. That is to say, I have given the reader an opportunity to work out practical, typical problems such as arise in everyday chess in over the board play. The reactions of readers of these earlier books have indicated that chess players welcome active participation rather than passive sponging up of ideas presented in predigested form.

The present work has been written with the primary purpose of providing an intensive drill for players who desire to improve their combinative skill. Instead of presenting principles and examples in the time-honored form, I have varied the procedure by giving each reader a chance to find the proper play through his own unaided efforts. He is not supplied the basic idea of each combination—he must find it for himself, just as he must find it in his own games. The reader is not told the precise goal of each combination—he must discover it by himself, just as in his own games. *Whatever the goal may be, he must find the most economical method in each instance.*

The 300 problems have been divided into three categories: easy, intermediate and frankly difficult. Thus each grouping becomes progressively more arduous as the reader proceeds on his way. He may grade himself on each quiz in the following manner:

MASTER STRENGTH: 18 out of 20 correct solutions.

CLUB PLAYER STRENGTH: 16 out of 20 correct solutions.

AMATEUR STRENGTH: 14 out of 20 correct solutions.

AVERAGE STRENGTH: 10 to 13 out of 20 correct solutions.

Most readers will fall into the last group. Anyone who fails to solve half of these problems correctly, should thereby be spurred on to obtain additional experience and devote himself to further study. In any event, any reader who studies these problems with the requisite care should be able to increase his combinative skill considerably.

FRED REINFELD

FIRST QUIZ

1

BLACK

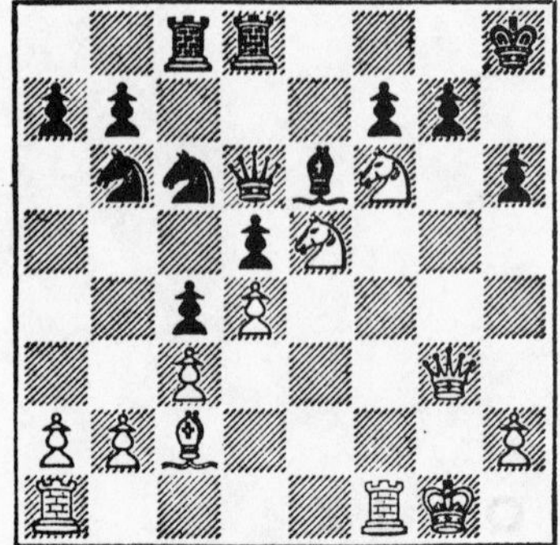

WHITE

White moves

2

BLACK

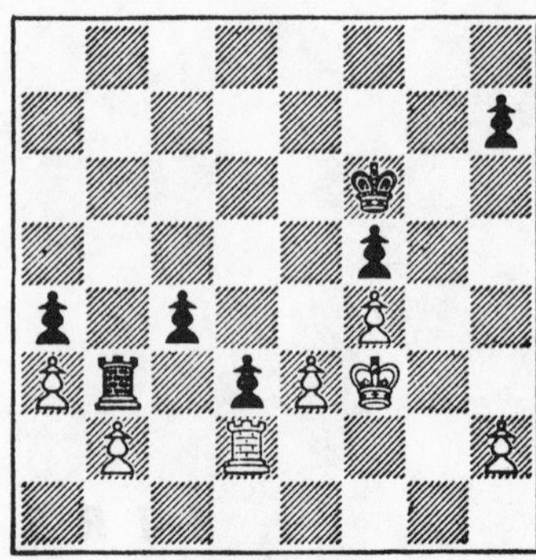

WHITE

Black moves

3

BLACK

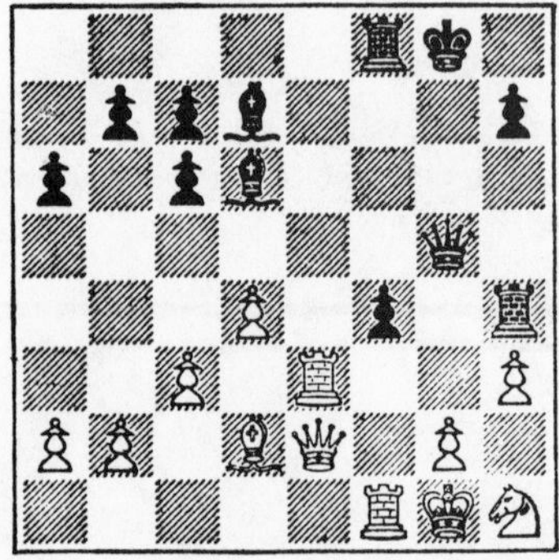

WHITE

White moves

4

BLACK

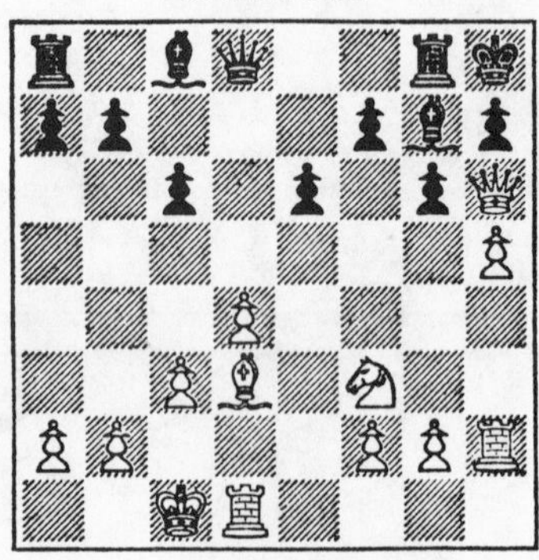

WHITE

White moves

1. From a simultaneous exhibition by Yates.
2. An early Spielmann combination.
3. A win from Reshevsky's child prodigy days.
4. How does White save the menaced Queen?

5

BLACK

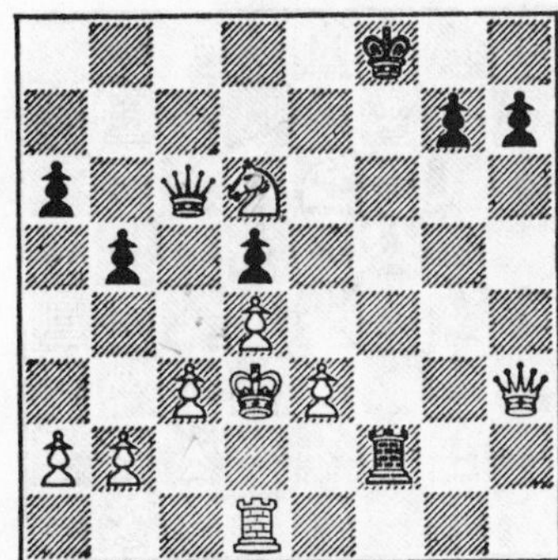

WHITE
Black moves

6

BLACK

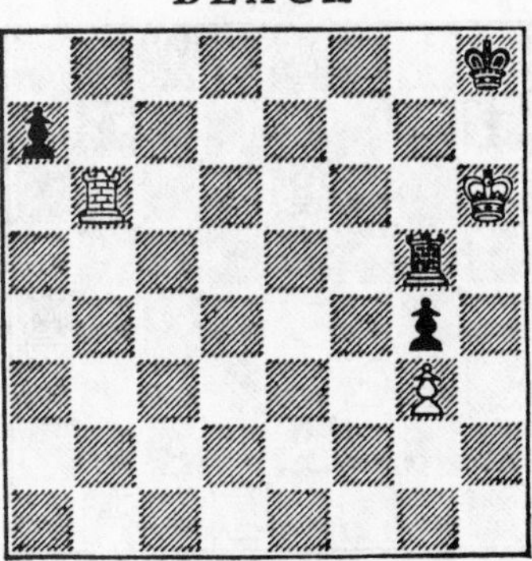

WHITE
White moves

7

BLACK

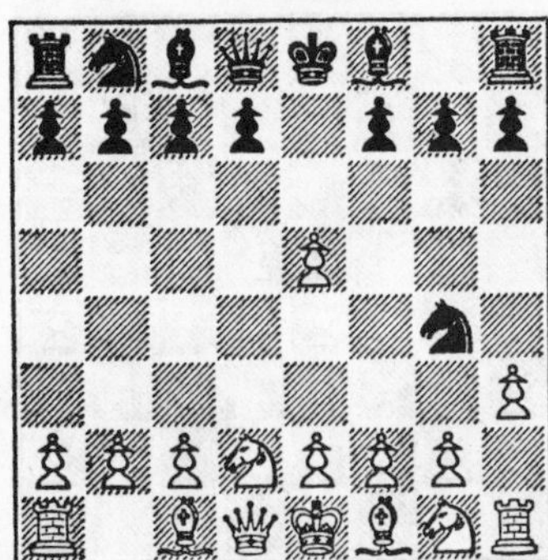

WHITE
Black moves

8

BLACK

WHITE
White moves

5. Think twice here!
6. A deceptively simple position. White's play is amazingly economical.
7. A "harmless" position.
8. Occupation of the seventh rank is the key to the win.

9

BLACK

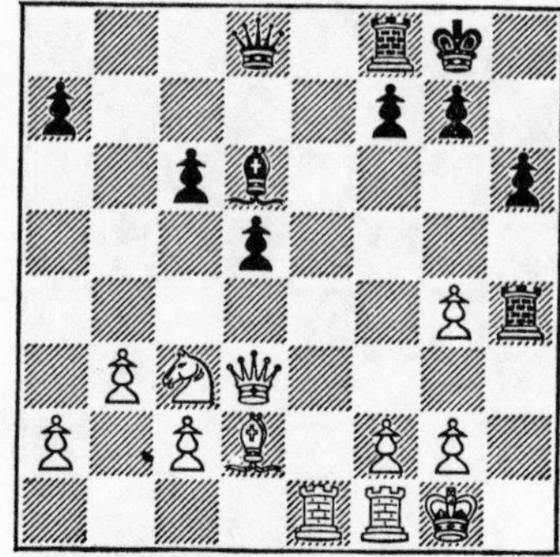

WHITE

Black moves

10

BLACK

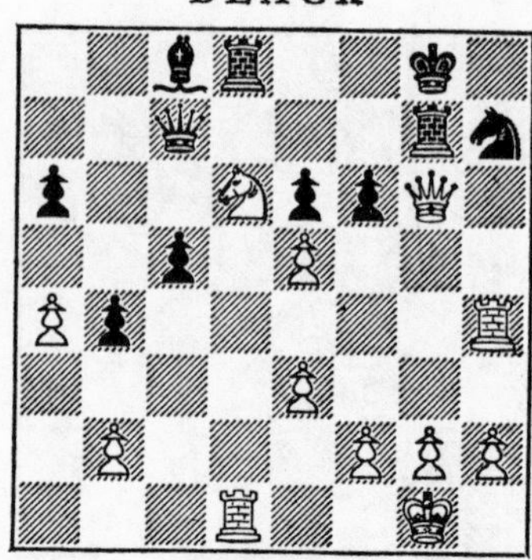

WHITE

White moves

11

BLACK

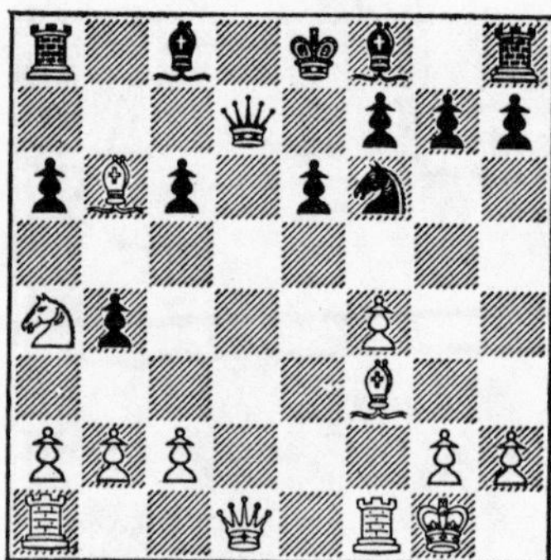

WHITE

White moves

12

BLACK

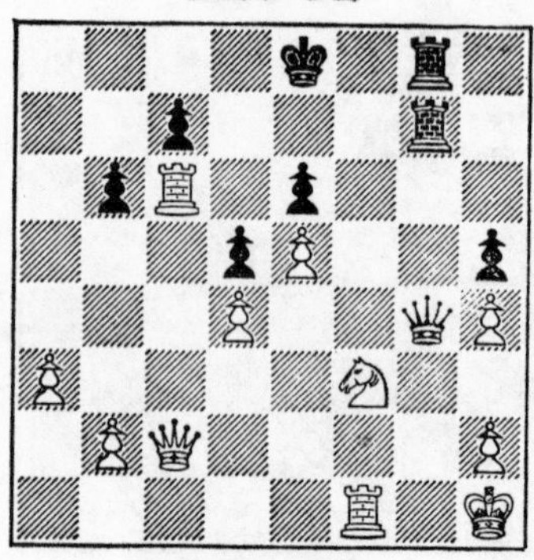

WHITE

Black moves

9. The winning method requires precision.
10. White is a piece down and his Queen is attacked.
11. White's lead in development tells.
12. Is Black's position worth a piece?

13

BLACK

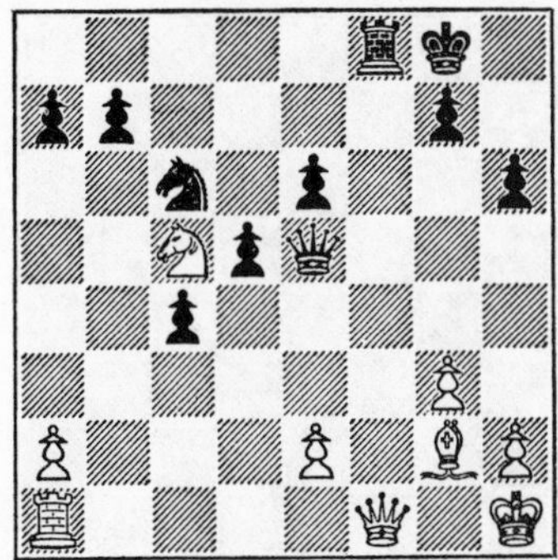

WHITE

White moves

14

BLACK

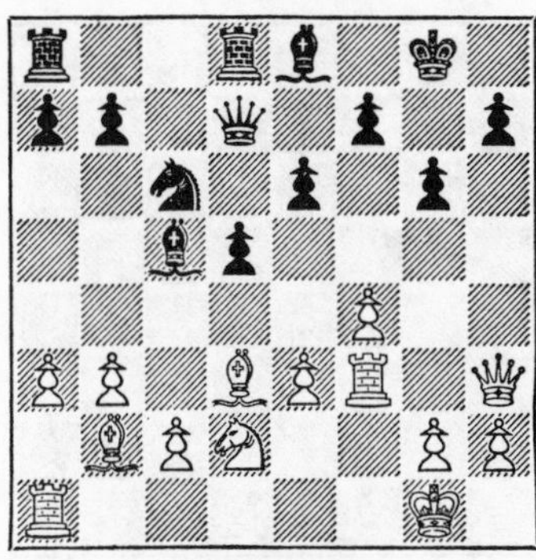

WHITE

White moves

15

BLACK

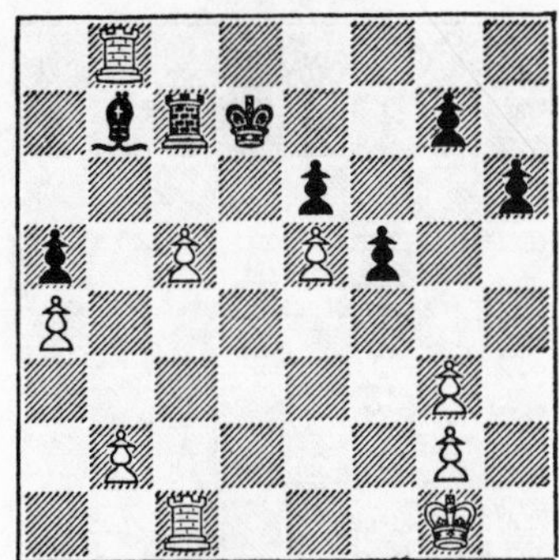

WHITE

White moves

16

BLACK

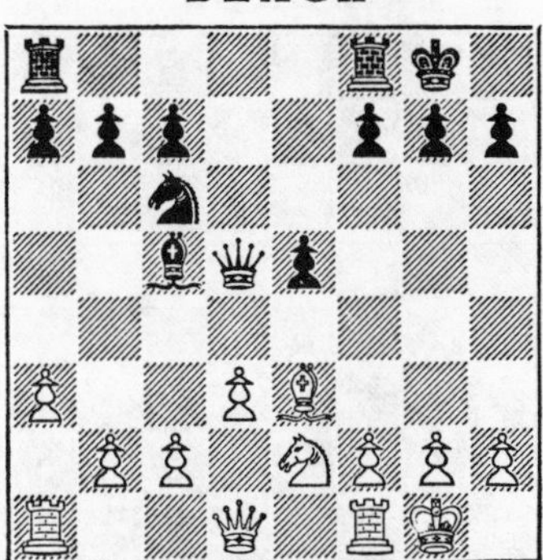

WHITE

White moves

13. From a Tarrasch Defense to the Queen's Gambit.
14. Can White exploit the critical weakness of Black's King-side?
15. White's Rooks are very strong.
16. Awkward development is quickly punished. Instructive play by White.

17

BLACK

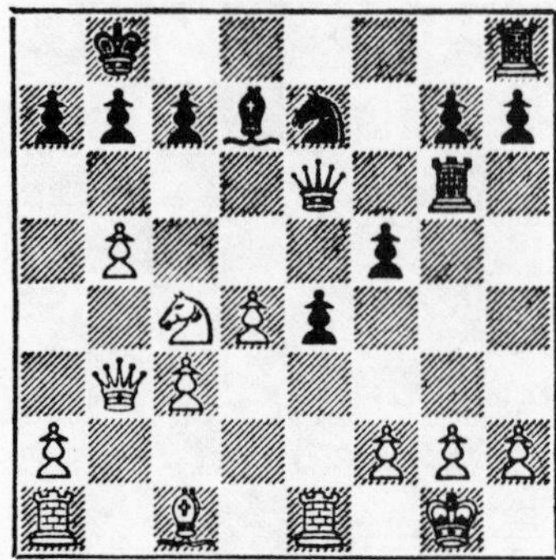

WHITE

White moves

18

BLACK

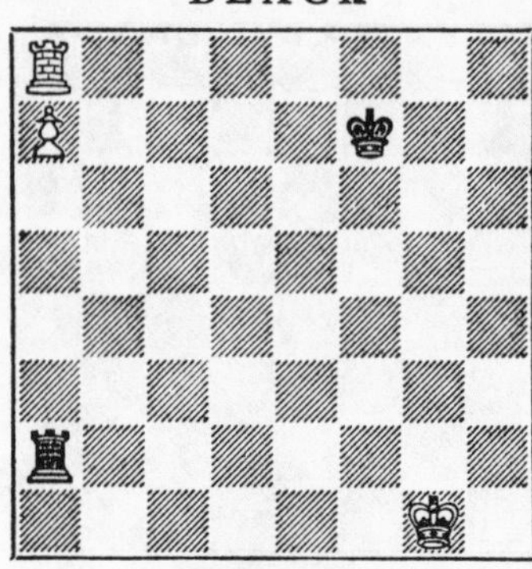

WHITE

White moves

19

BLACK

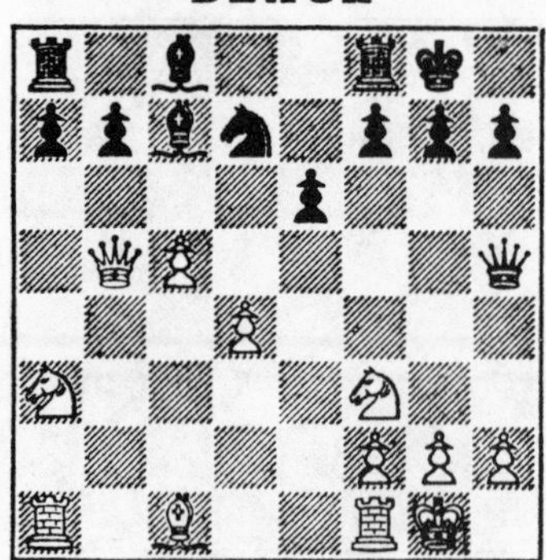

WHITE

White moves

20

BLACK

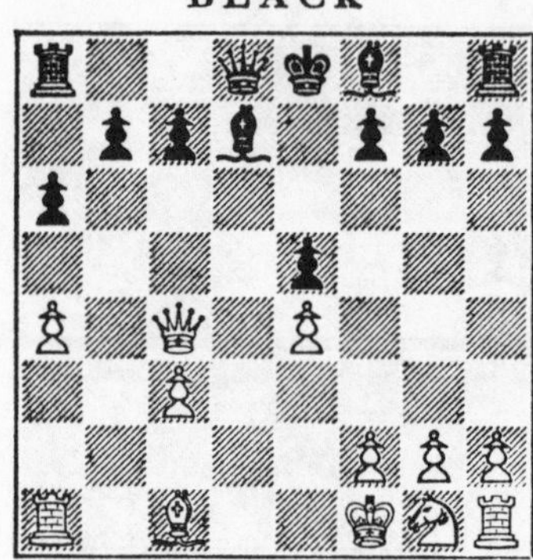

WHITE

Black moves

17. White takes advantage of the clumsy position of his opponent's pieces.
18. There is only one winning move!
19. A typically piquant Tartakover winning move.
20. A pretty win by one of the younger Russian masters.

FIRST QUIZ

1. White has an overwhelming attacking position and can win in many ways. The quickest and most elegant is *1* Q—Kt6! leaving Black helpless.

2. Black wins easily with *1* . . . R×KtP! *2* R×R, P—B6; *3* R—Kt6 *ch,* K—K2; *4* R—QB6, P—B7 (not 4 . . . P—Q7? 5 K—K2 and White wins) and White has no defense against 5 . . . P—Q7.

3. White wins with the interesting move *1* R—Kt3.

4. White plays *1* Q×P *ch!* K×Q; *2* P×P *mate!* Obvious but pretty.

5. Black's command of the seventh rank leads to a surprising finish: *1* . . . Q—B5 *ch!* *2* Kt×Q, KtP×Kt *mate.*

6. At first sight, one would take this "simple" position for a sure draw. And yet: *1* R—Kt7! and Black must resign! For if *1* . . . R—Kt1; *2* R—R7 *mate;* if the Rook moves along the fourth rank, then *2* R—Kt8 *ch* also leads to mate.

7. Curiously enough, Black wins the Queen with *1* . . . Kt—K6! for if *2* P×Kt, Q—R5 *ch* forces mate.

8. White wins neatly with *1* R—B7! giving Black the sad choice of giving up his Queen or being mated.

9. Here is a combination often encountered in actual play: *1* . . . B—R7 *ch;* *2* K—R1, B—Kt6 *ch;* *3* K—Kt1, R—R8 *ch!* *4* K×R, Q—R5 *ch;* *5* K—Kt1, Q—R7 *mate.* Note that *1* . . . R—R8 *ch!* *2* K×R, Q—R5 *ch* fails because of *3* Q—R3.

10. White has given up a piece for the attack, but he regains it with interest by playing *1* R×Kt! Black has no good reply, for example *1* . . . R×Q; *2* R×Q, B—Q2; *3* Kt—Kt7; or *1* . . . P×P; *2* R×R *ch,* Q×R; *3* Q×Q *ch,* K×Q; *4* Kt—B5 *ch,* etc.

11. *1* B×P! is decisive: Black is mated, or he must lose the Queen.

12. White's forces are scattered and his Rook on B1 is overburdened. The result: *1* . . . Q×Kt *ch!* and Black forces mate.

13. Black has three Pawns for a piece and apparently a promising game. However, *1* Q×R *ch!* K×Q; *2* Kt–Q7 *ch* is decisive.

14. Here is a variant of a frequently seen sacrifice: *1* Q×P *ch!* K×Q; *2* R–R3 *ch,* K–Kt1; *3* R–R8 *mate.* Black's negligence in leaving the long diagonal denuded of protection proved fatal.

15. A simple case of double attack: *1* R×B, R×R; 2 P–B6 *ch.*

16. Black seems to have an excellent game, but he loses a piece in a manner which is as neat as it is unexpected: *1* Kt–B3, Q–Q3; *2* Kt–K4. Black was at fault here in not providing more carefully for the security of his Bishop.

17. White wins the exchange with *1* Kt–K5; if *1* . . . R–B3; *2* B–Kt5 does the trick; if *1* . . . Q×Q; *2* P×Q, R–Q3; *3* Kt–B7, etc.

18. White wins with *1* R–R8, R×P; *2* R–R7 *ch.* Black can postpone the decision for a while by checks with his Rook, during which White's King approaches the Rook to put an end to the checks. A classic endgame position.

19. White wins a piece with *1* P–B6!, taking advantage of the unprotected state of Black's Queen.

20. Black wins with *1* . . . B–Kt4! pinning the Queen and also threatening . . . Q–Q8 *mate.*

SECOND QUIZ

21

BLACK

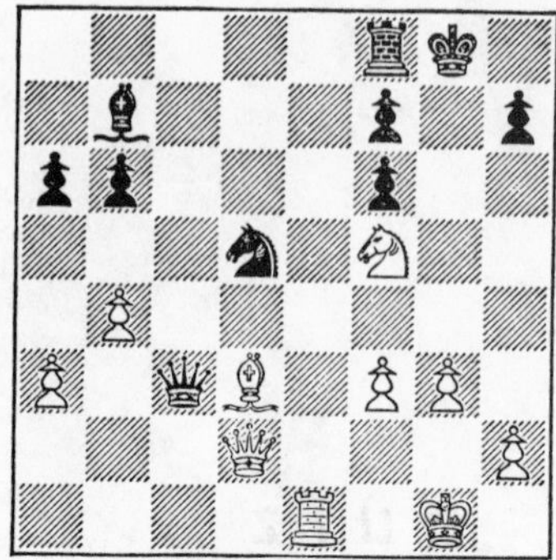

WHITE

White moves

22

BLACK

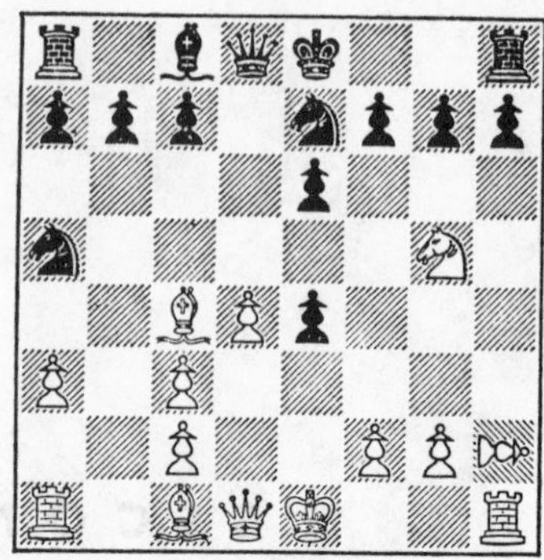

WHITE

White moves

23

BLACK

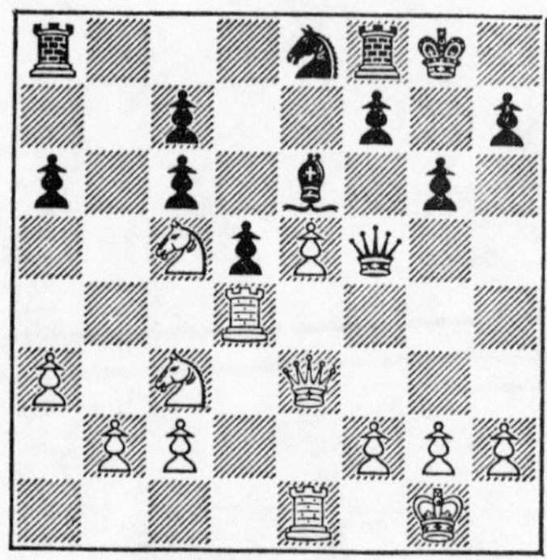

WHITE

White moves

24

BLACK

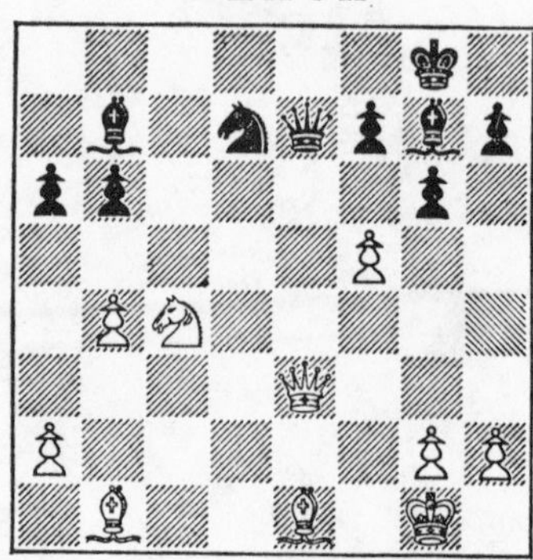

WHITE

Black moves

21. Spielmann finds a nonchalant winning move.
22. An ancient theme in ultramodern form. The Black QKt is in danger!
23. A quick win for Dr. Bernstein.
24. Apparently a position barren of resources for both players.

25

BLACK

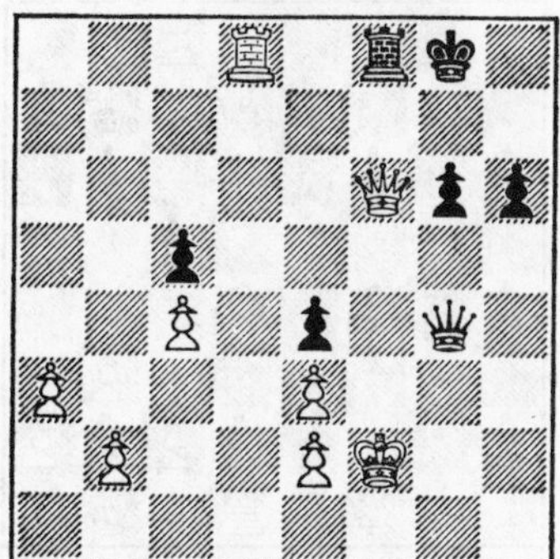

WHITE

Black moves

26

BLACK

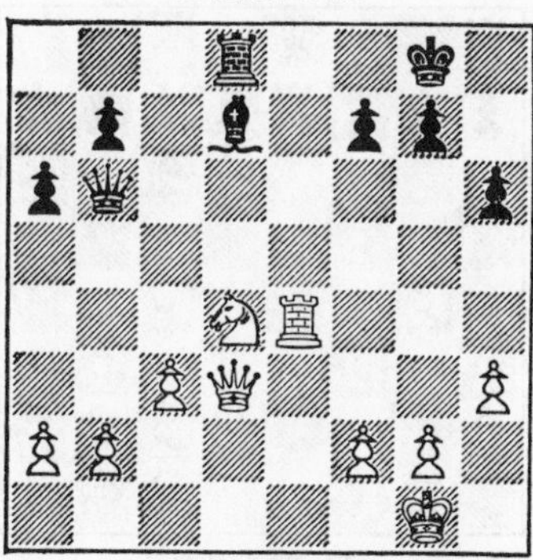

BLACK

Black moves

27

BLACK

WHITE

White moves

28

BLACK

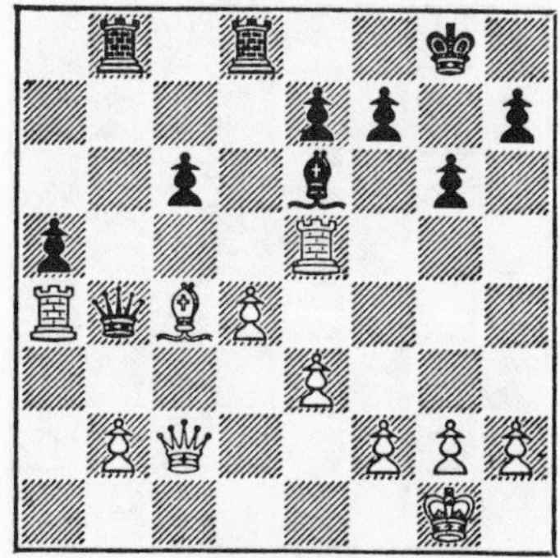

WHITE

Black moves

25. White is in trouble—or is he?
26. This one was missed by Torre who was in great time pressure.
27. A critical position—it is do or die for White.
28. Black has a decisive continuation, overlooked by two strong players.

29

BLACK

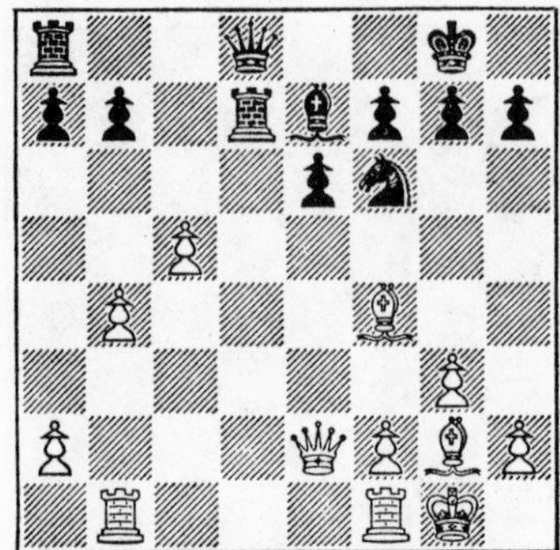

WHITE

White moves

30

BLACK

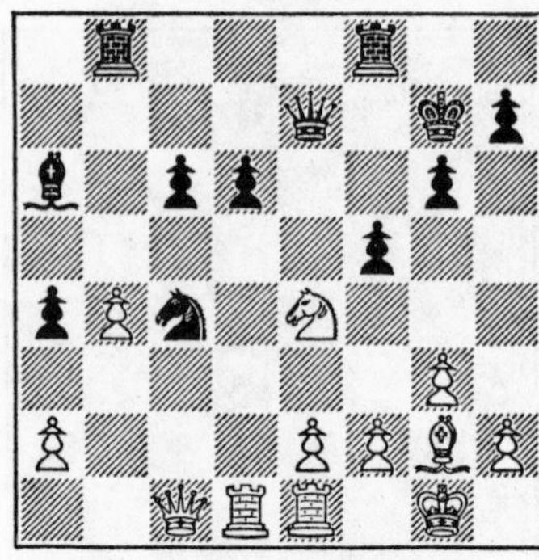

WHITE

White moves

31

BLACK

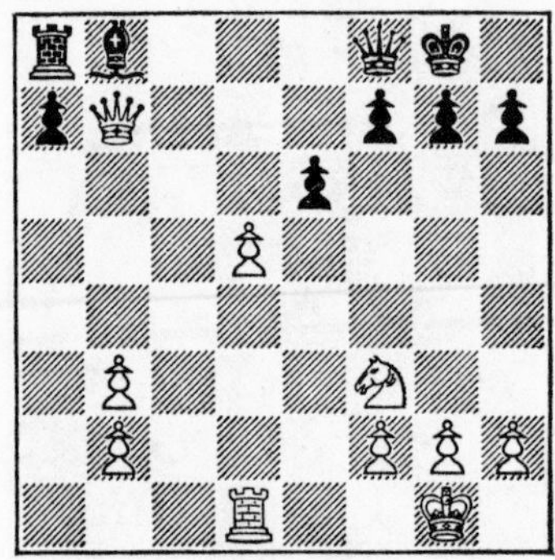

WHITE

White moves

32

BLACK

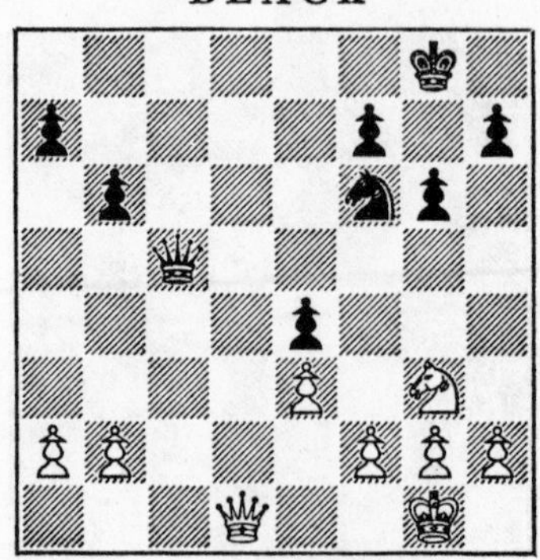

WHITE

White moves

29. Fine reveals the power of the two Bishops.
30. White wins material with a neat move.
31. White has two winning continuations.
32. Euwe wins a Pawn by a clever maneuver.

33

BLACK

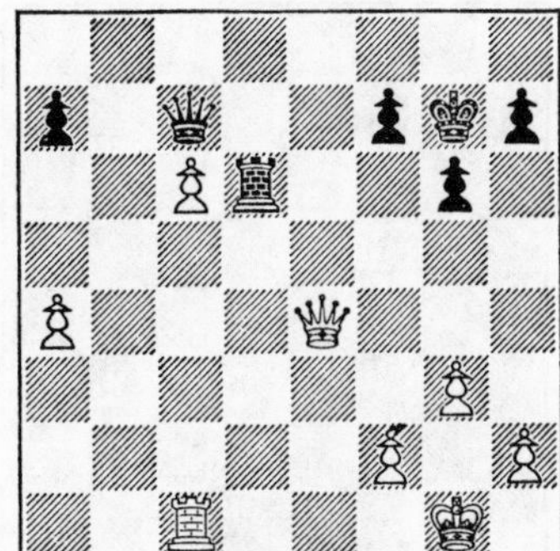

WHITE

White moves

34

BLACK

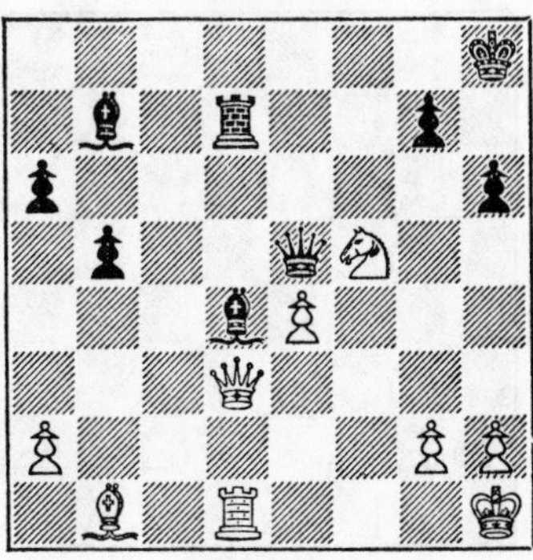

WHITE

Black moves

35

BLACK

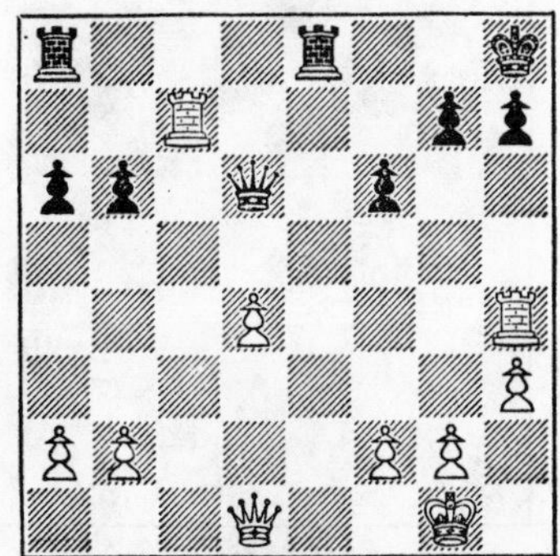

WHITE

White moves

36

BLACK

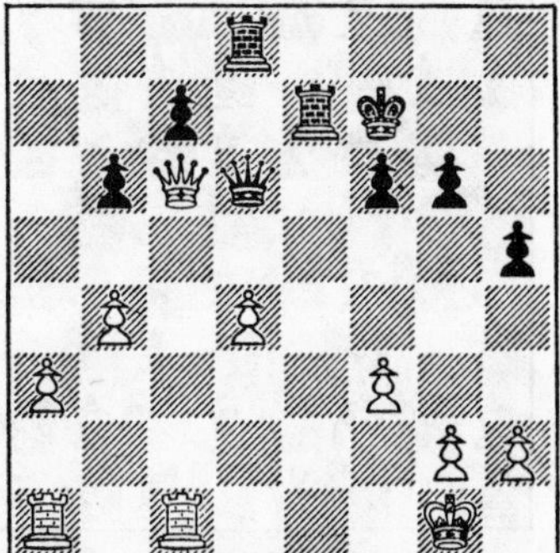

WHITE

Black moves

33. A Capablanca win.
34. Black resigned in this position! What did he miss?!
35. Another win missed in actual play.
36. Is this position as level as it looks?

37

BLACK

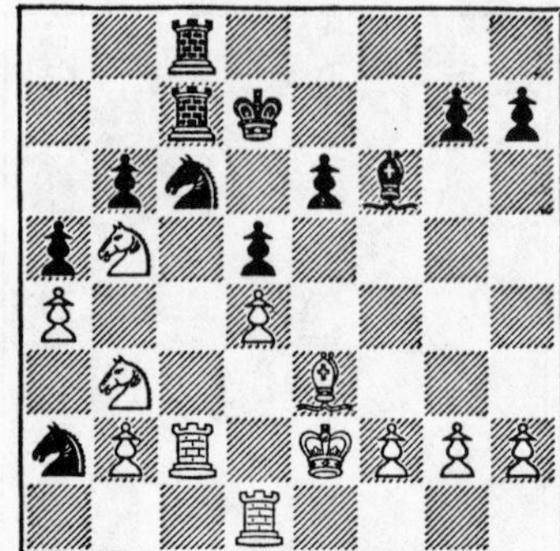

WHITE

Black moves

38

BLACK

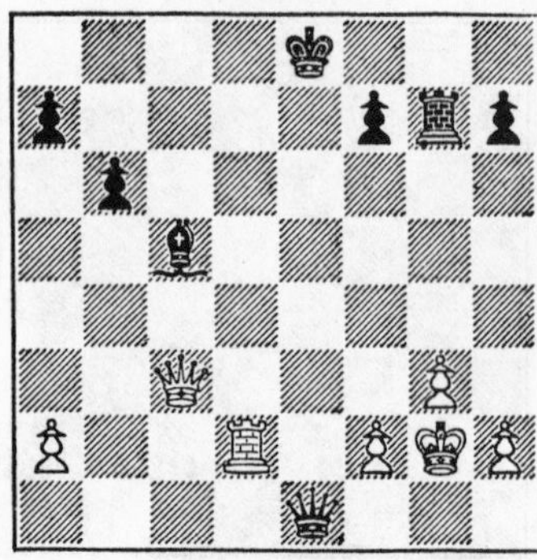

WHITE

White moves

39

BLACK

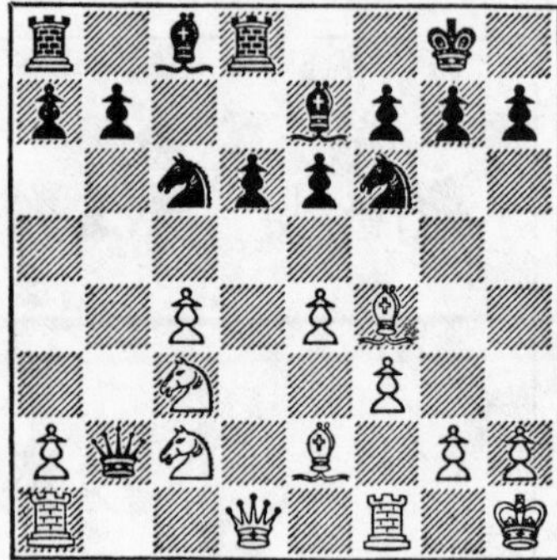

WHITE

White moves

40

BLACK

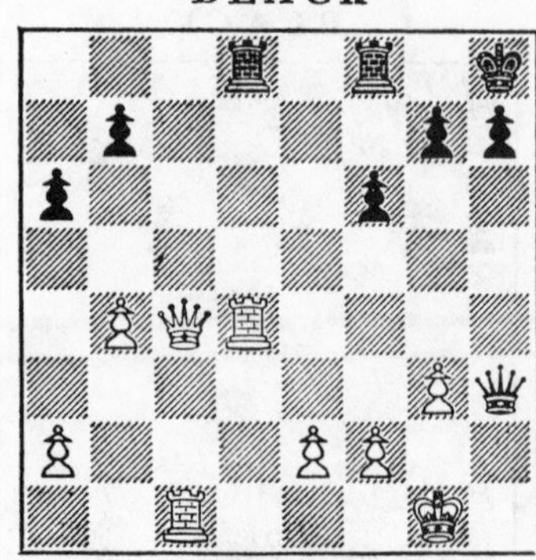

WHITE

Black moves

37. Should Black rely on defense or attack?
38. Euwe wins against Stoltz—from a Hastings Christmas Tourney.
39. Black has gobbled the QKtP.
40. White is apparently secure, but he has overlooked something.

SECOND QUIZ

21. White plays the debonair *1* Q—R6! for after *1* . . . Q×R *ch; 2* B—B1 Black is helpless.

22. White wins a Pawn in familiar fashion with *1* Kt×BP, K×Kt; *2* Q—R5 *ch,* etc.

23. Black's position is very inferior, but one would hardly expect his immediate downfall with *1* P—KKt4! Q×BP; *2* R—Q2 and the Queen is lost!

24. Black wins the Queen by *1* . . . B—Q5! for if *2* Q×B, Q×B *mate.*

25. White has hoped to salvage his pinned Queen by pinning the pinning Rook (!) but Black upsets his calculations with *1* . . . Q—R5 *ch.*

26. Black wins by means of the double pin *1* . . . B—B4!

27. Black's attack seems to be crushing, but White has two ways of escaping. The solution: *1* Q—B8 *ch!* R×Q; *2* R×R *mate.* There is a second way, which, however, only draws, and cannot therefore be considered the proper solution: *1* R×R, Q×R *ch; 2* R—B1, R×P *ch; 3* K×R, Q×Q; *4* Kt—B7 *ch,* K—Kt1; *5* Kt—R6 *ch,* etc.

28. Black wins with *1* . . . Q—K8 *ch; 2* B—B1, B—Kt6. This win was missed in actual play.

29. White utilizes the power of his Bishops to win the exchange with *1* P—B6!

30. White takes advantage of his opponent's weak Pawn position to win a Pawn with *1* Kt×P, Kt×Kt; *2* Q×P, etc.

31. White has two winning methods: *1* P—Q6! B×P; *2* R×B and White is a piece to the good. The second winning method is even more curious: *1* Q×R! B×P *ch; 2* K×B, Q×Q; *3* P–Q6, P–B3; *4* P–Q7, Q–Q1; *5* Kt–K1, K–B2; *6* Kt–B2, P–QR4 (White threatened Kt–Kt4 with decisive effect); *7* P–QKt4! P–R5; *8* P–Kt5 and wins.

32. A neat forking combination: *1* Q–Q8 *ch,* K–Kt2; *2* Q×Kt *ch,* K×Q; *3* Kt×P *ch* and White, with a Pawn to the good, wins the ending easily.

33. White removes the blockader with *1* Q–K5 *ch* and *2* Q×R.

34. From a famous game in which Black resigned at this point because he saw no way to save his Bishop. *1* . . . B–Kt8! would have won White's Queen.

35. *1* R×P *ch!* forces mate in a few moves. Overlooked in actual play.

36. *1* . . . R–K8 *ch!* is decisive. This is a kind of combination for which there are numerous opportunities.

37. Black wins a Pawn with *1* . . . Kt×P *ch!* Many players would be so intent on removing the Black Rook from attack that they would miss this trick.

38. White has just sacrificed a piece in order to win Black's Queen with *1* R–Q8 *ch.*

39. Black's Queen has wandered far afield. *1* Kt–R4! wins the Queen—drastic punishment for Pawn-grabbing.

40. White's pieces are very awkwardly situated. Black exploits this with *1* . . . R–B1, winning the Queen.

THIRD QUIZ

41

BLACK

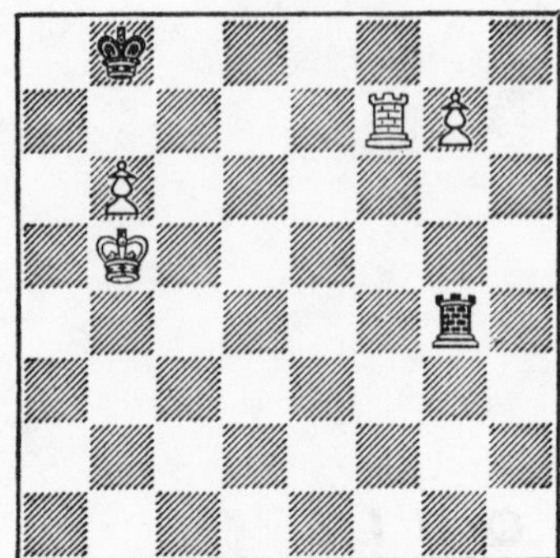

WHITE
White moves

42

BLACK

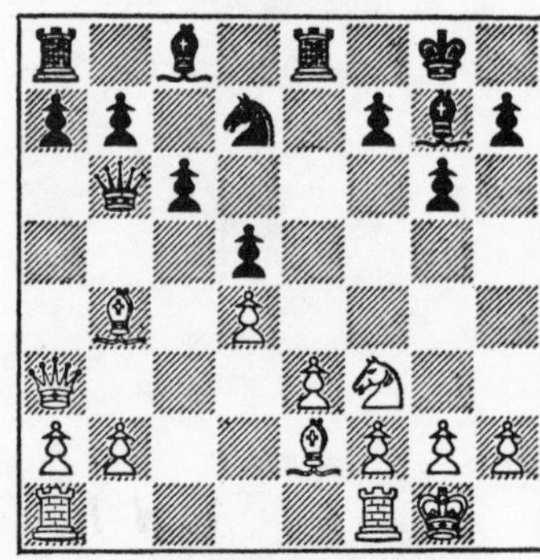

WHITE
White moves

43

BLACK

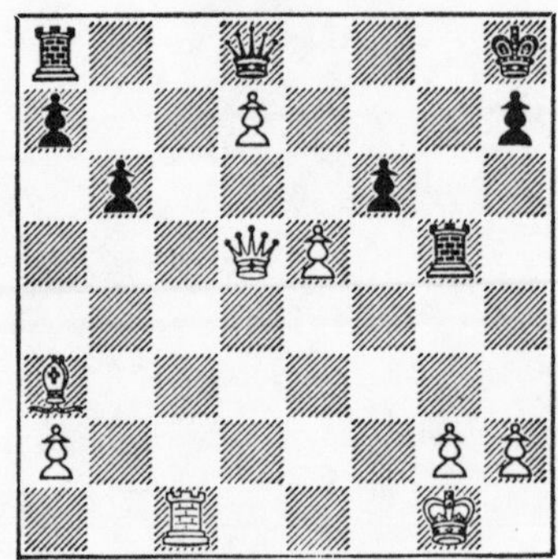

WHITE
White moves

44

BLACK

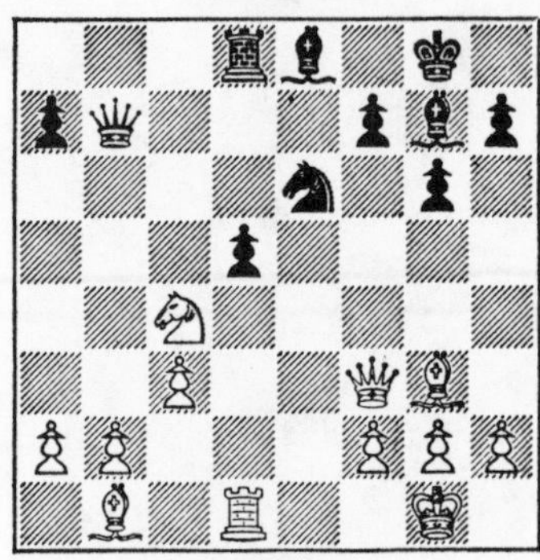

WHITE
Black moves

41. White must be careful!
42. White's Bishops are all-powerful as Black finds to his cost.
43. White has two winning lines.
44. Black is not hampered by the pin.

45

BLACK

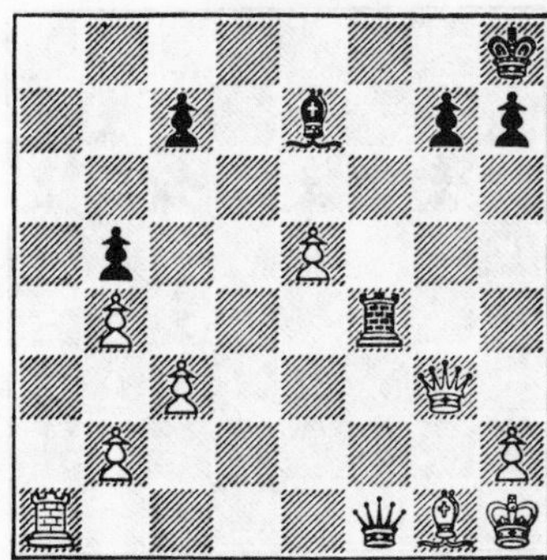

WHITE
Black moves

46

BLACK

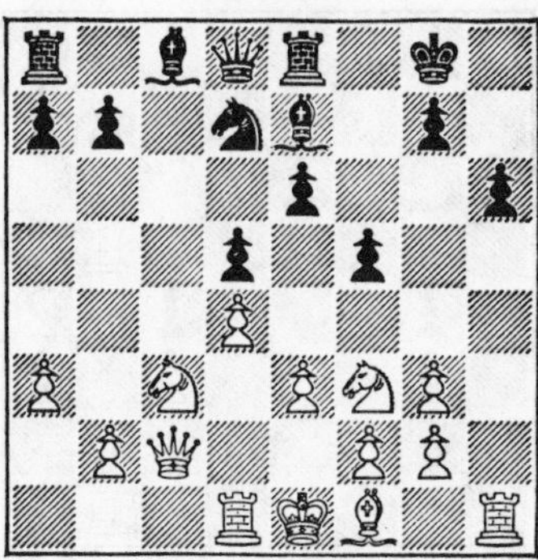

WHITE
White moves

47

BLACK

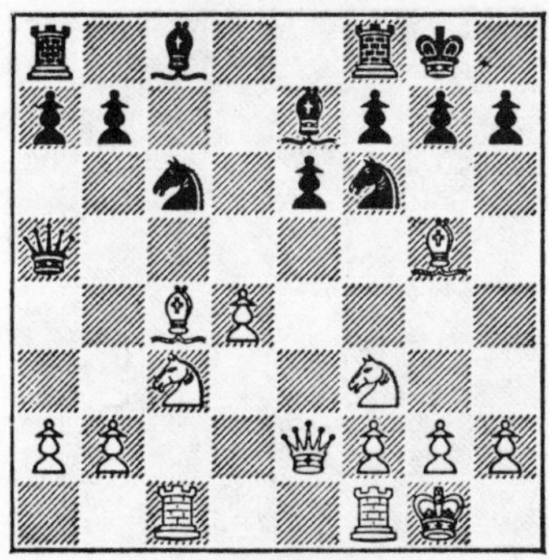

WHITE
Black moves

48

BLACK

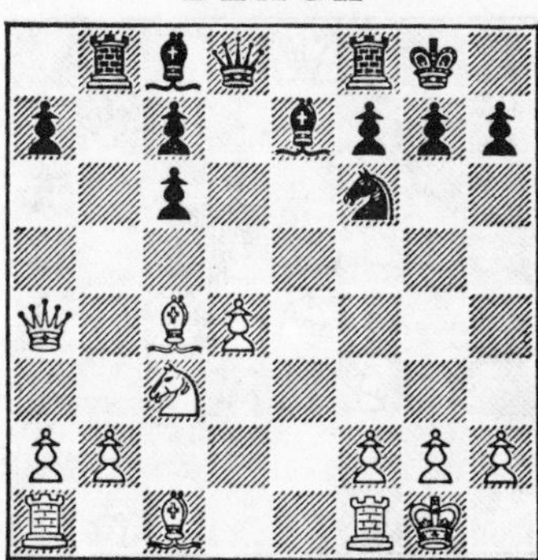

WHITE
Black moves

45. Another win which was overlooked by first-rate players.

46. A harmless-looking position(?).

47. Just how secure is White's position?

48. White's Queen has wandered far afield. The refutation is simple.

49

BLACK

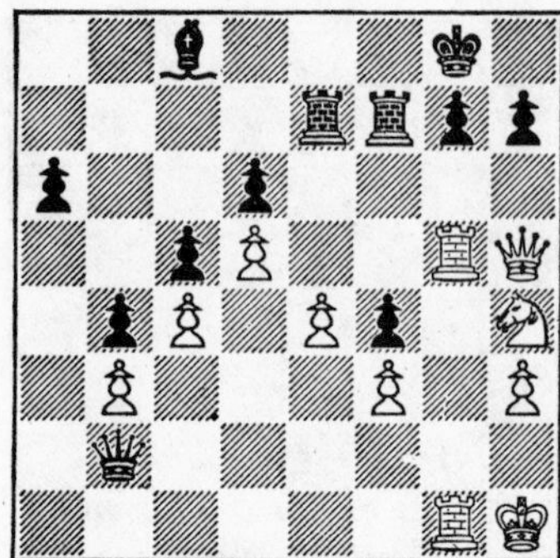

WHITE

White moves

50

BLACK

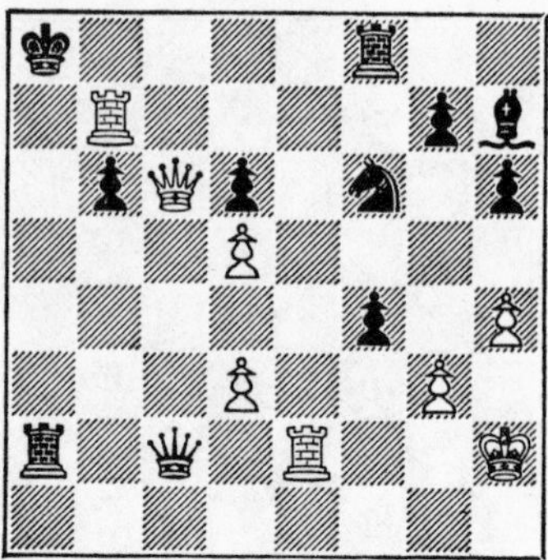

WHITE

White moves

51

BLACK

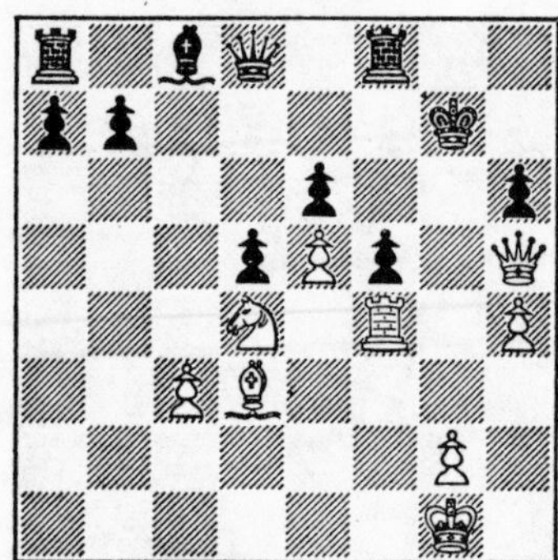

WHITE

White moves

52

BLACK

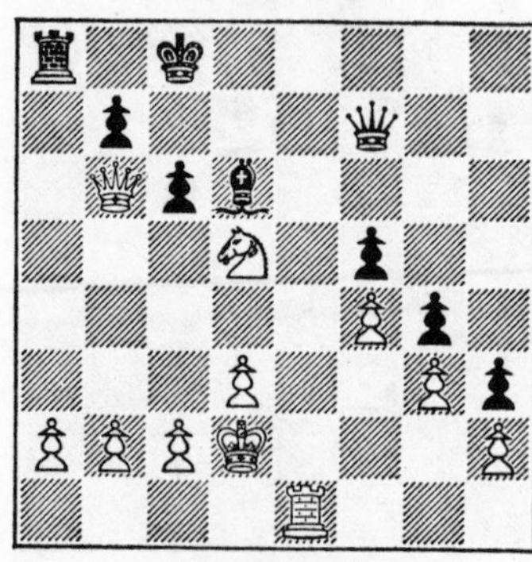

WHITE

White moves

49. Here it is Black's Queen that has wandered far afield.
50. An amazingly simple solution!
51. A pretty Tarrasch win.
52. White wins on the seventh rank. The theme often gives rise to artistic play.

53

BLACK

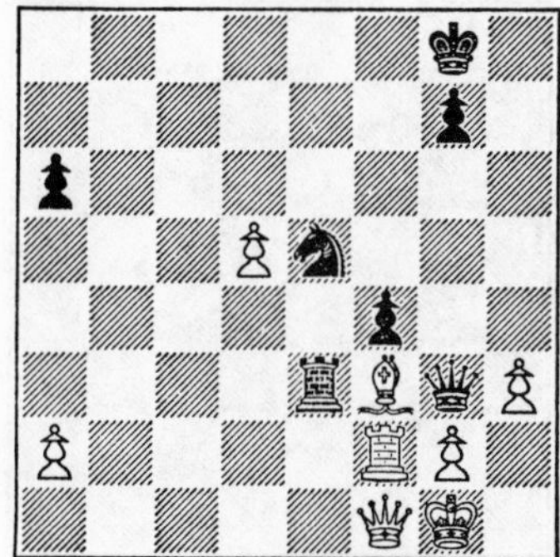

WHITE
Black moves

54

BLACK

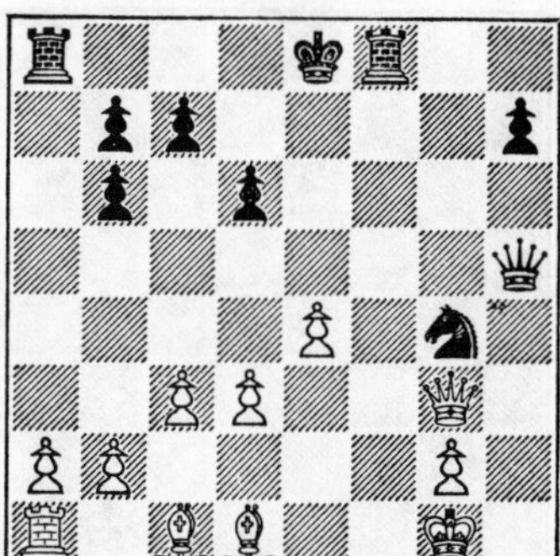

WHITE
Black moves

55

BLACK

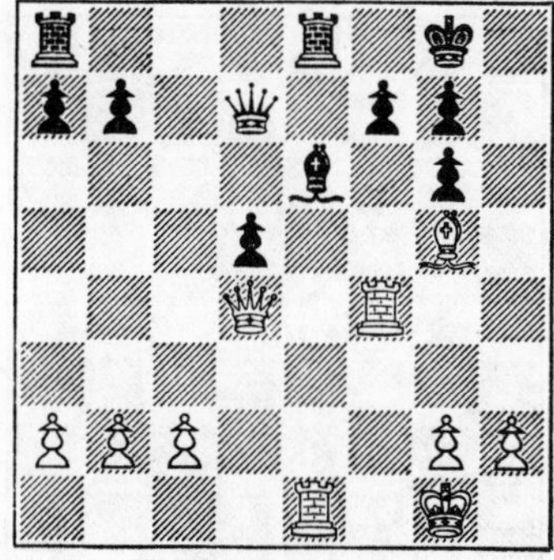

WHITE
White moves

56

BLACK

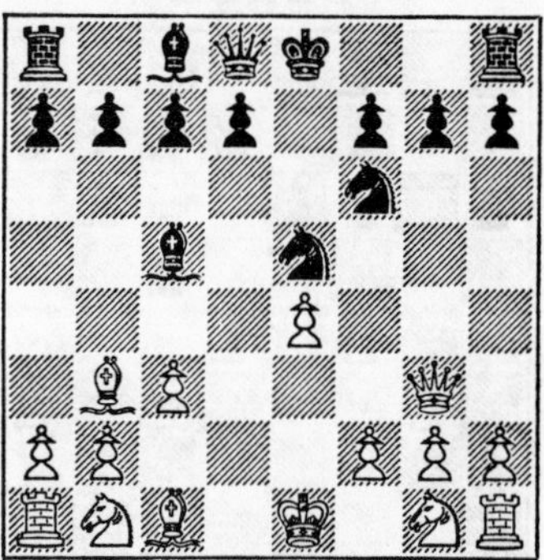

WHITE
Black moves

53. Clever and indirect utilization of a pinning motif.

54. Black missed a pretty win here.

55. An astonishing combination, but an easy one to find.

56. An elegant combination decides.

57

BLACK

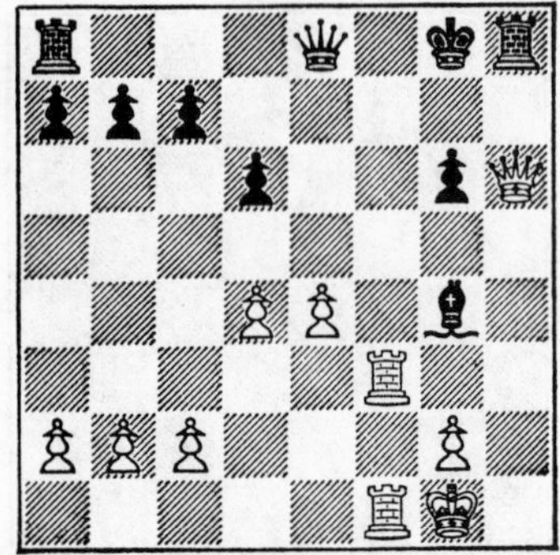

WHITE

White moves

58

BLACK

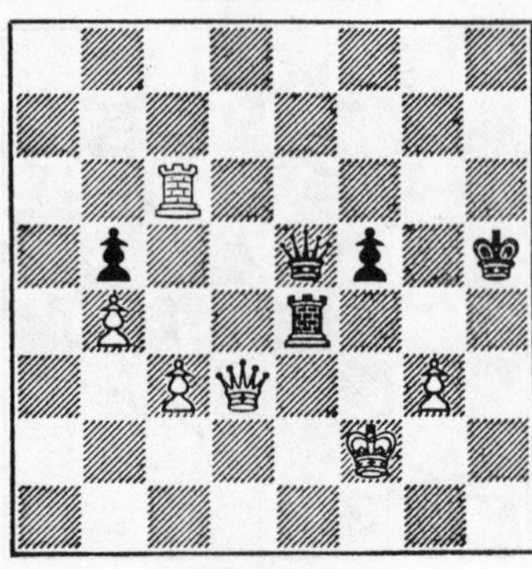

WHITE

White moves

59

BLACK

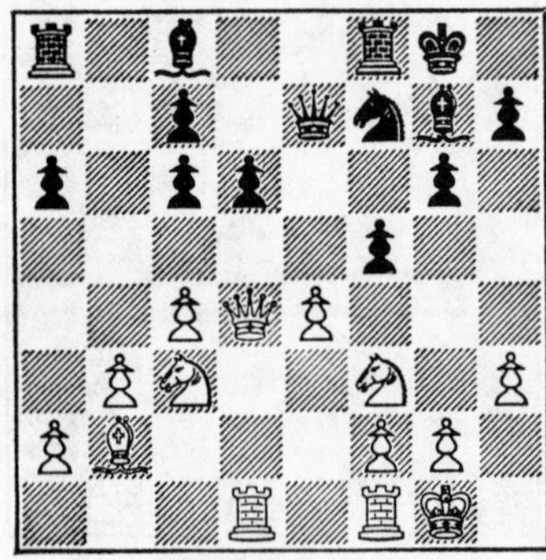

WHITE

White moves

60

BLACK

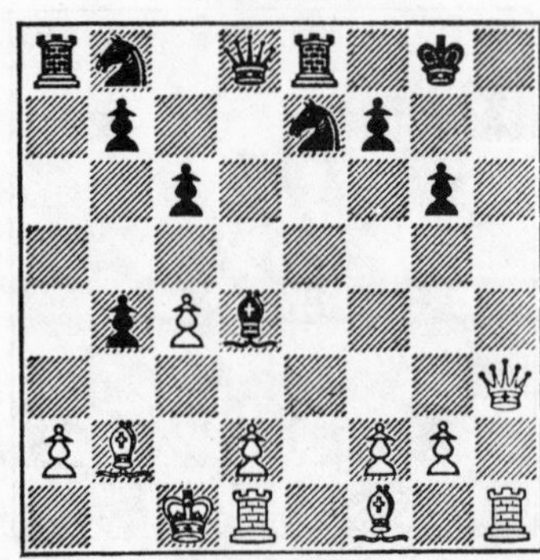

WHITE

White moves

57. A Morphy classic.
58. Black succumbs quickly. The finish is surprisingly drastic.
58. There is a right way and a wrong way to try to win here.
60. An early Euwe win.

THIRD QUIZ

41. White can win with *1* P—Kt7 and then moving his King to the King-side in reply to repeated checks; or he can win by moving his King at once. He must beware of 1 R—B8 ch, K—Kt2; 2 P—Kt8(Q)? R×Q; 3 R×R and Black is stalemated.

42. White wins a piece with *1* B—R5, B—B1 (else the Queen is lost); *2* Q—B3, B—Kt5; *3* B or Q×B.

43. White wins with *1* Q×R, Q×Q; *2* R—B8 *ch,* R—Kt1; *3* R×Q, R×R; *4* P—K6, etc. Another way is *1* B—K7!

44. The great Steinitz has just played Kt×BP? relying on the fact that the QP is pinned. Black calmly replies *1* . . . P×Kt! since White cannot play 2 Q×Q? R×R *mate!*

45. Black wins a Rook with *1* . . . Q×R, *for if 2* Q×R, Q—R1 *ch* and mate follows. Very curious!

46. Despite the seemingly harmless appearance of the position, White plays *1* Kt—QKt5 and there is no way to ward off the loss of the exchange.

47. *1* . . . Kt×P wins a Pawn. White's KKt is overburdened.

48. Black wins at least a piece with *1* . . . R—Kt5, *for if* 2 Q×BP, B—Kt2.

49. The sacrifice of White's Queen is decisive: *1* Q×P *ch!* K×Q; *2* R—R5 *ch,* K—Kt1; *3* Kt—Kt6, R—B3; *4* R—R8 *ch,* K—B2; *5* R—B8 *mate.*

50. White wins simply and elegantly with *1* R×QKtP *ch,* Q×Q; *2* R×R *ch* and mate next move.

51. Black seems to have a solid defensive position, but *1* R—Kt4 *ch!* crushes all further resistance.

52. White wins the Queen by playing *1* R—K7!

53. Black wins the Queen by playing *1* . . . R—K8! 2 Q×R, Kt×B *ch.* An effective example of no less than three pins.

54. Black overlooked that he could force mate in two with . . . Q—R8 *ch!* etc.

55. White forces a curious mate with *1* Q×P *ch!* K×Q; 2 B—B6 *ch* followed by *3* R—R4, etc.

56. A remarkable position. Black wins the Queen by *1* . . . B×P *ch!* If *2* K×B, Kt×P *ch;* if *2* Q×B, Kt—Q6 *ch.* An amusing example of the Knight's forking powers.

57. A Morphy finish: *1* R—B8 *ch,* Q×R; *2* R×Q *ch,* R×R; *3* Q×P *mate!*

58. White wins with *1* Q—Q1 *ch,* K—Kt4; *2* Q—Q2 *ch,* P—B5 (King moves lead to a quick mate); *3* R—B5 winning Black's Queen.

59. White wins a piece with *1* Kt—Q5! Note that the "brilliant" *1* Q×B *ch* would not achieve the same objective, for if *1* . . . K×Q; 2 Kt—Q5 *ch,* Q—K4, etc.

60. This seems to be one of those positions in which there is an interesting struggle between attack and counter-attack. Actually White mates in two: *1* Q—R8 *ch!* B×Q; 2 R×B *mate.*

FOURTH QUIZ

61

BLACK

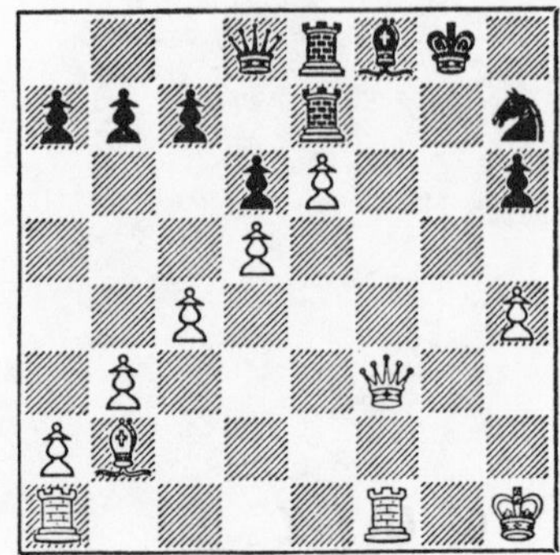

WHITE

White moves

62

BLACK

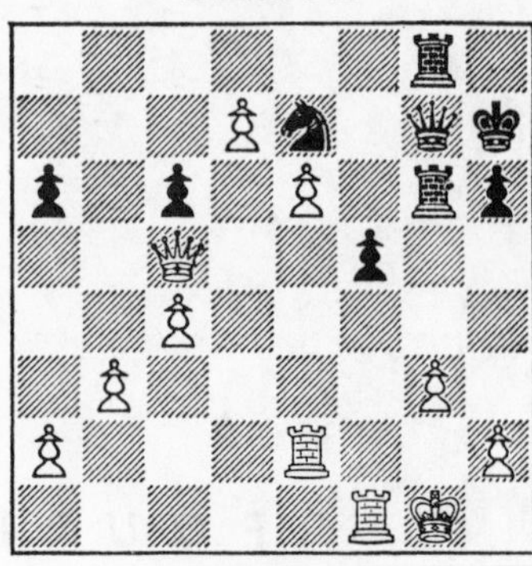

WHITE

Black moves

63

BLACK

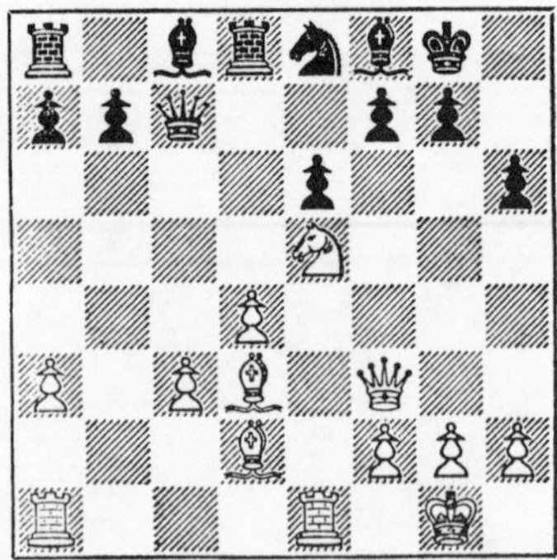

WHITE

White moves

64

BLACK

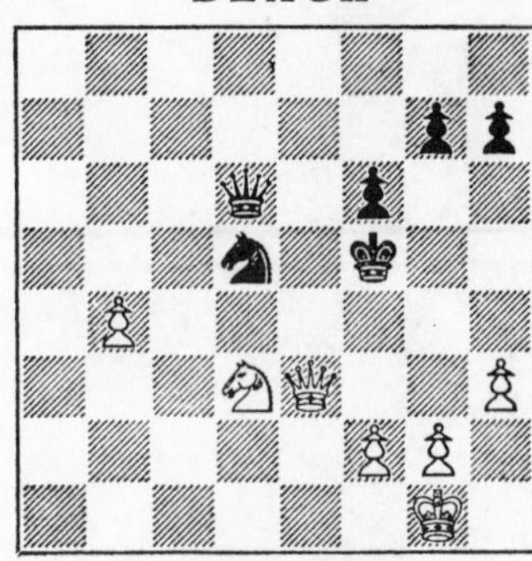

WHITE

White moves

61. White's Bishop is an interested spectator.
62. Black has time for a counterattack.
63. Black's setup is solid but not safe!
64. White wins with amazing rapidity.

65

BLACK

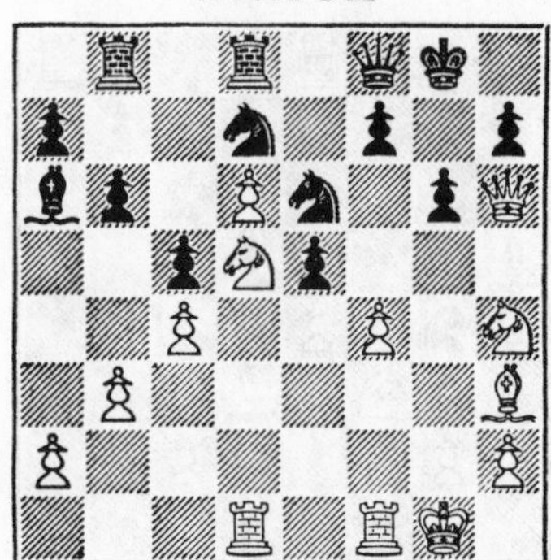

WHITE
White moves

66

BLACK

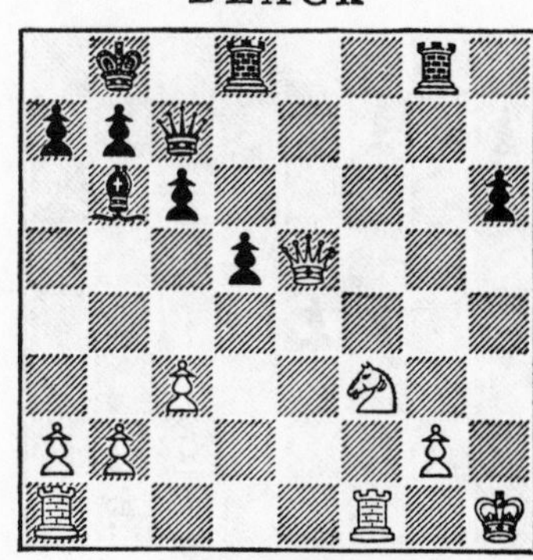

WHITE
Black moves

67

BLACK

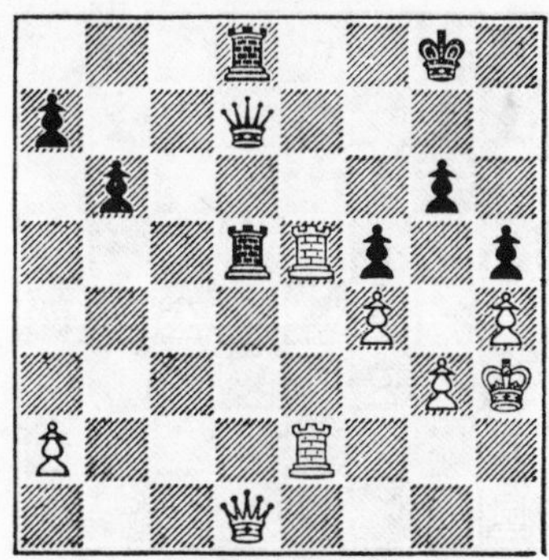

WHITE
White moves

68

BLACK

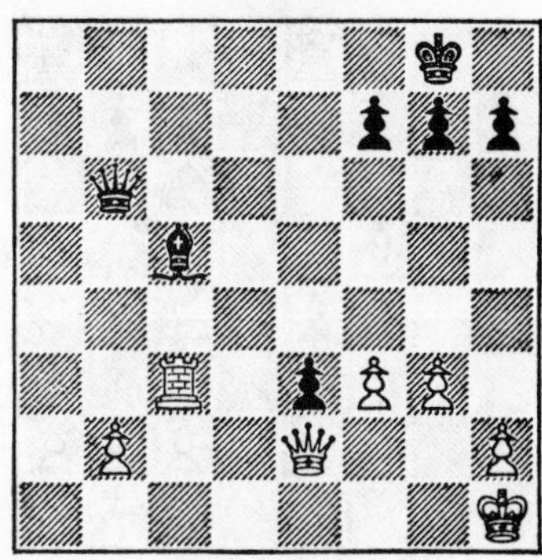

WHITE
White moves

65. Vidmar wins energetically.
66. Black's first move is paradoxical. Hence it may be difficult to find.
67. One of those positions which seem barren of possibilities.
68. The Bishop is lost!

69

BLACK

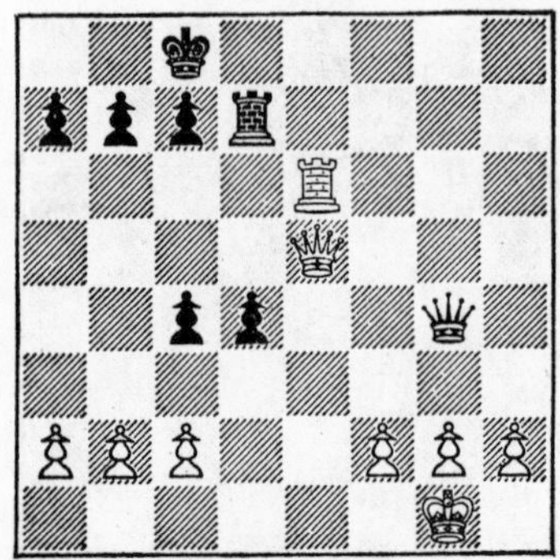

WHITE
White moves

70

BLACK

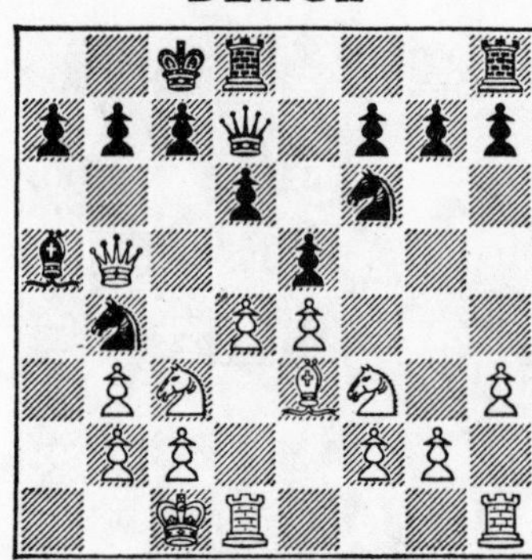

WHITE
Black moves

71

BLACK

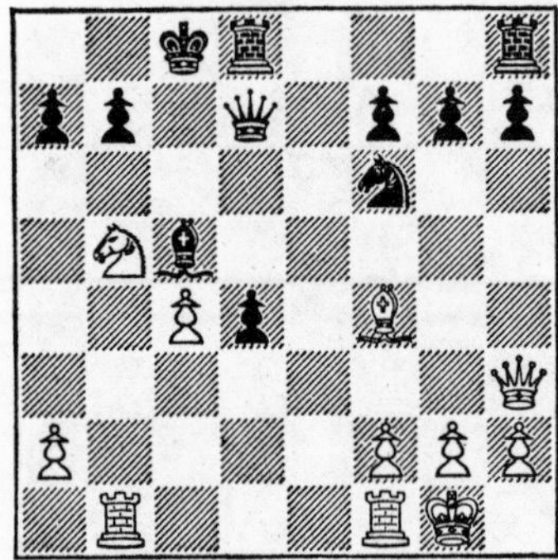

WHITE
White moves

72

BLACK

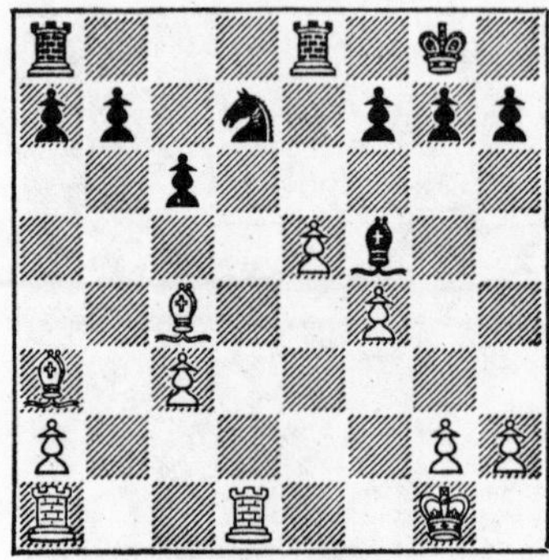

WHITE
White moves

69. Easy—but tricky!
70. White's Queen is out on a limb. The consequences are catastrophic.
71. Flohr must resign in short order!
72. The mighty Lasker decides the issue at once.

73

BLACK

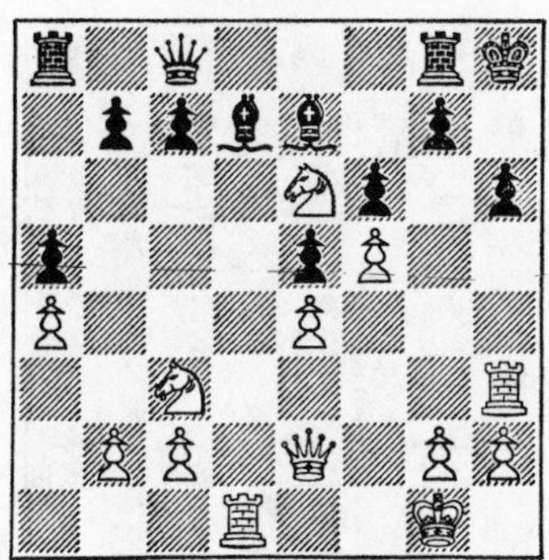

WHITE

White moves

74

BLACK

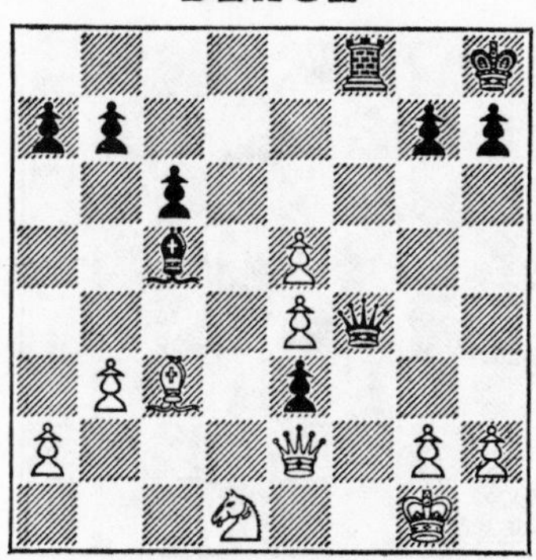

WHITE

Black moves

75

BLACK

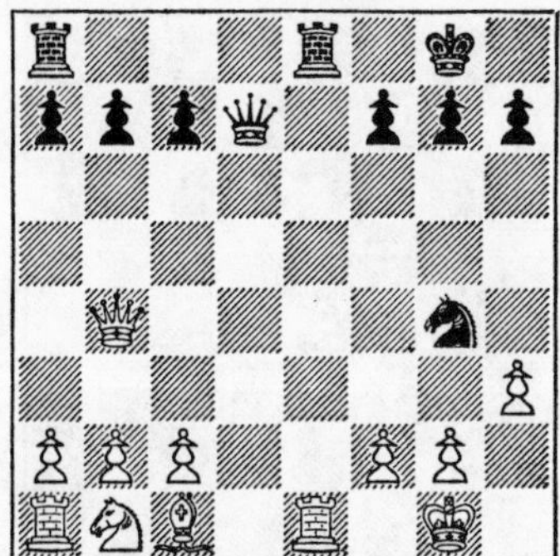

WHITE

Black moves

76

BLACK

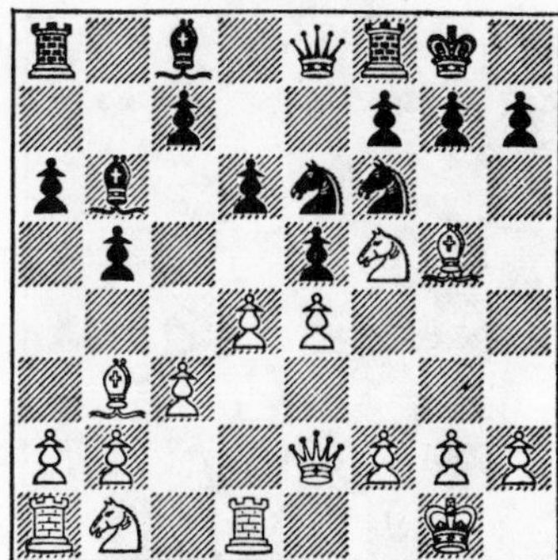

WHITE

White moves

73. Another Morphy classic.
74. Find the strongest move for Black's Queen. The underlying idea is of great practical value.
75. Double attack forces the win.
76. Rubinstein is forced to resign when the game has barely started.

77

BLACK

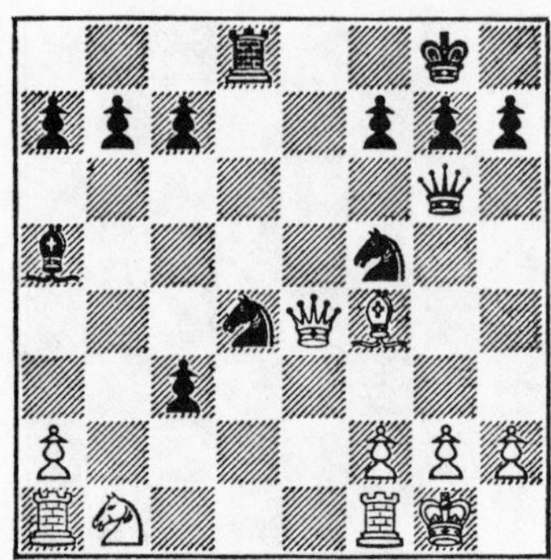

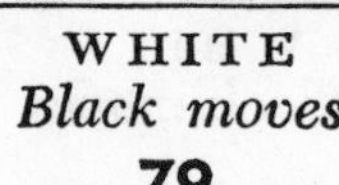

WHITE

Black moves

78

BLACK

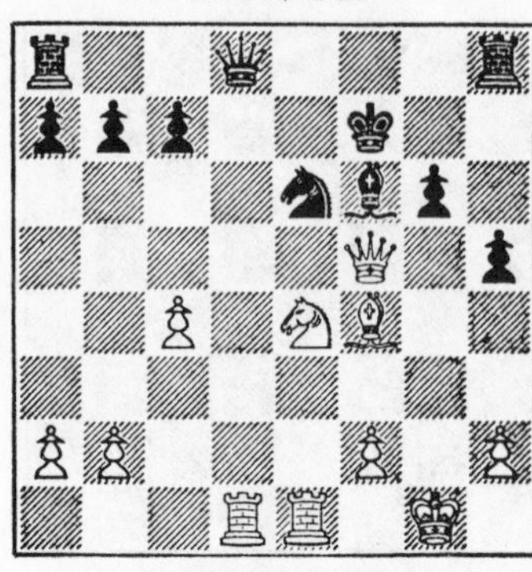

WHITE

White moves

79

BLACK

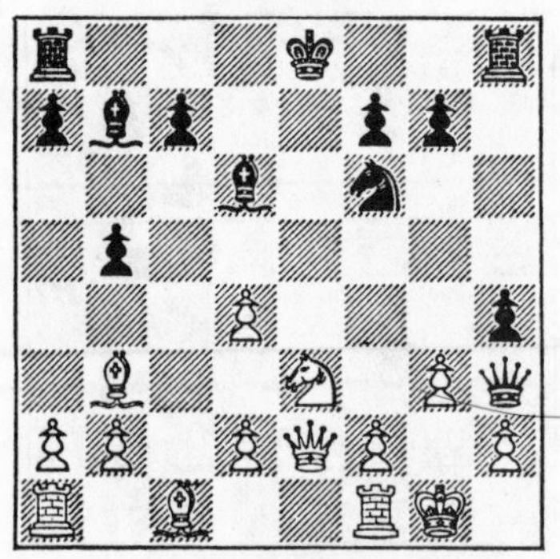

WHITE

Black moves

80

BLACK

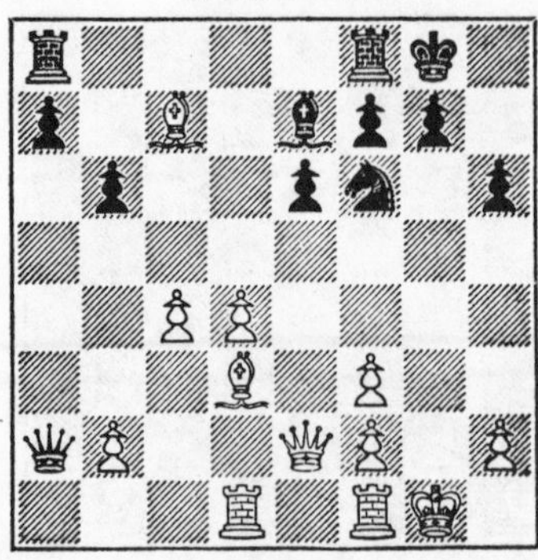

WHITE

White moves

77. Morphy shows his virtuosity with the Knights.
78. White seems to have nothing better than exchanging Queens.
79. Rubinstein utilizes the heavy concentration of Black's forces.
80. Tarrasch finds a quickly decisive continuation.

FOURTH QUIZ

61. The open position of Black's King allows a startling finish: *1* Q—B7 *ch,* R×Q; *2* P×R *mate.*

62. Despite the menace of the advanced Pawns, Black calmly stops to win a Pawn with *1 . . .* R×P *ch!* Capture of the Pawn would lead to mate, so that White must decline the "gift."

63. Taking advantage of Black's defective development, White plays *1* Kt×P! If *1 . . .* Q×Kt? *2* B—R7 *ch* wins the Queen.

64. In this harmless-looking position, White has a surprising mate: *1* P—Kt4 *ch,* K—Kt3; *2* Q—K8 *ch* and *3* Q—R5 *mate.*

65. White wins the Queen with *1* Kt—K7 *ch,* K—R1; 2 either Kt×P *ch,* etc.

66. Black wins a piece with *1 . . .* Q×Q; *2* Kt×Q, R—Kt4; *3* Kt—B3, R—R4 *ch; 4* Kt—R2, B—B2, etc.

67. A characteristic combination in such positions: *1* R×R, Q×R; *2* R—K8 *ch,* etc.

68. White makes use of Black's unprotected first rank with *1* Q×P! winning the Bishop!

69. White has a clever win: *1* P—KB3! Q—R5 (forced); *2* R—K8 *ch,* R—Q1; *3* Q—K6 *ch,* K—Kt1; *4* Q—Q7, Q—K8 *ch; 5* R×Q, R×Q; *6* R—K8 *ch* and mate next move.

70. White's Queen has wandered too far afield, as Black demonstrates with *1 . . .* Kt—R7 *ch; 2* K—Kt1 (or 2 K—Q2, Q×Q), Kt×Kt *ch* winning the Queen.

71. White scores neatly with *1* Kt×P *ch!!* B×Kt; *2* Q—R3.

If now *2 . . .* Kt—R4; *3* Q×B, Kt×B; *4* Q—R8 *ch* wins; if *2 . . .* P—QKt3; *3* R×P! wins.

72. White wins a piece with *1* P—K6!

73. White wins a piece with *1* Q—Q2 because of the double threat of *2* Q×P *ch* or *2* Q×B.

74. Black forces mate with *1 . . .* Q—B8 *ch; 2* Q×Q, P—K7 *ch.* White has not provided against a possible discovered check.

75. Black wins with the devastating *1 . . .* Q—Q3! White has no reply.

76. White wins with *1* QB×Kt, P×B; *2* B×Kt. If *2 . . .* B×B; *3* Q—Kt4 *ch* forces mate. If *2 . . .* P×B; *3* Q—Kt4 *ch,* Q—Kt3; *4* Kt—K7 *ch* wins the Queen. Black was at fault in allowing his King-side to be broken up—always a dangerous proceeding.

77. Black wins with *1 . . .* Kt—KKt6! The unprotected state of White's Queen proves fatal.

78. White decides the game with *1* Kt—Kt5 *ch,* Kt×Kt; *2* R—Q7 *ch.*

79. With Black's pieces concentrated on White's King, the following combination is almost a matter of course: *1 . . .* Q×RP *ch! 2* K×Q, P×P *ch; 3* K—Kt1, R—R8 *mate.*

80. Black has gone in for Pawn-grabbing, with the customary result: *1* R—R1, Q—Kt6; *2* B—B2, Q—Kt5 (or *2 . . .* Q×KtP; *3* B×P *ch*); *3* R—R4 and Black's Queen is trapped.

FIFTH QUIZ

81

BLACK

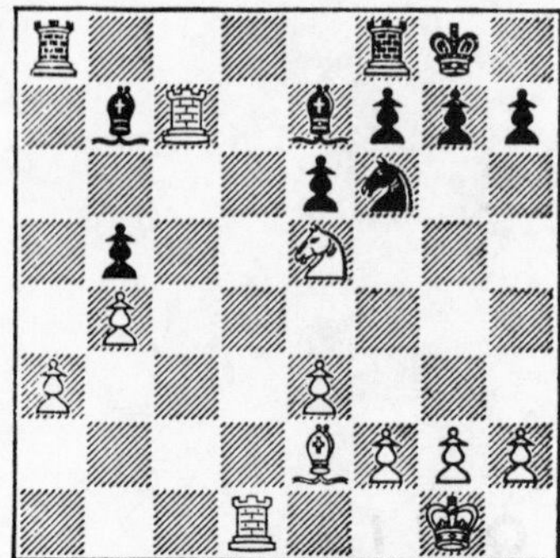

WHITE

Black moves

82

BLACK

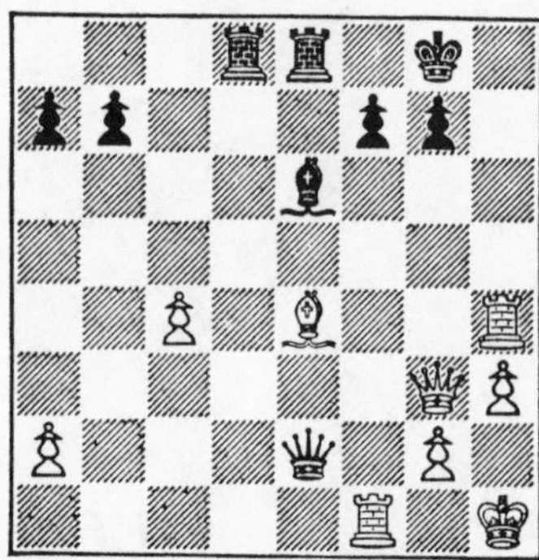

WHITE

White moves

83

BLACK

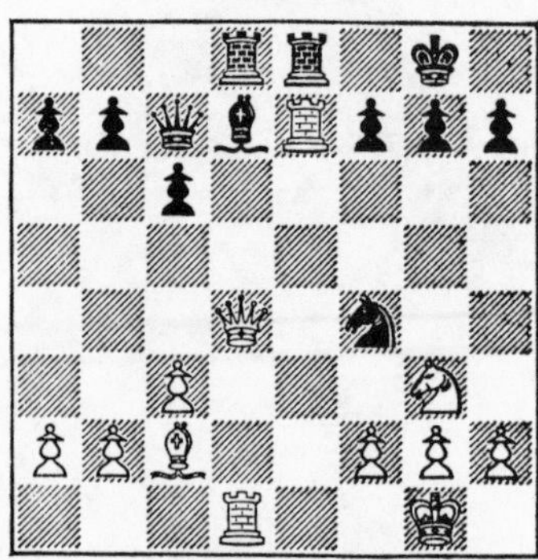

WHITE

White moves

84

BLACK

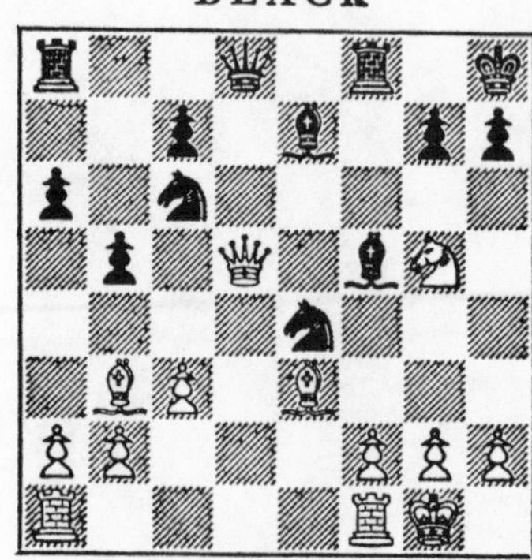

WHITE

White moves

81. Black has a clever resource.
82. With proper play, White's attack decides in short order.
83. Janowski finds an amusing finish.
84. An old motif in a novel form. Look for the strongest move!

85

BLACK

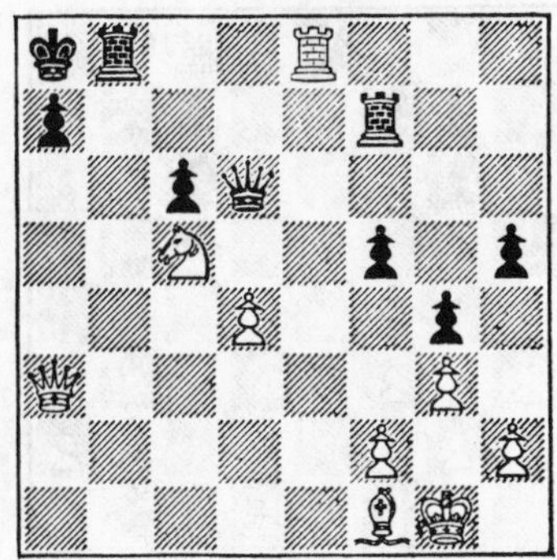

WHITE

White moves

86

BLACK

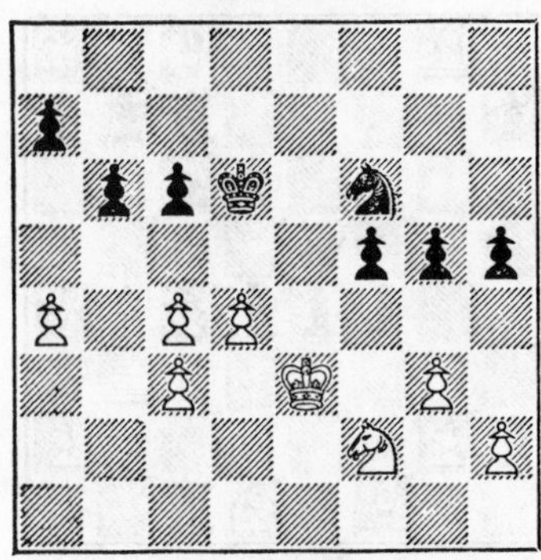

WHITE

Black moves

87

BLACK

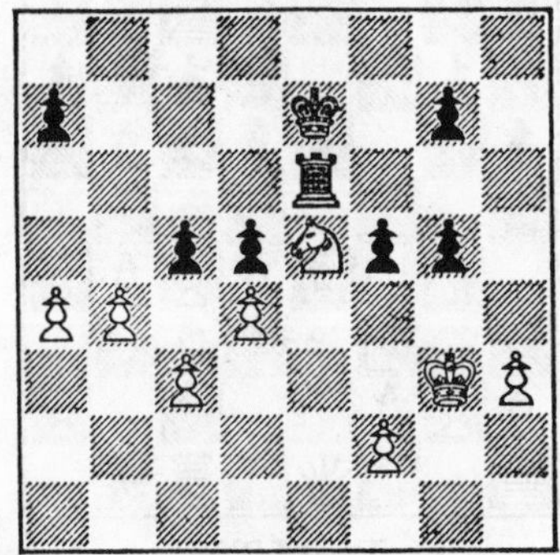

WHITE

Black moves

88

BLACK

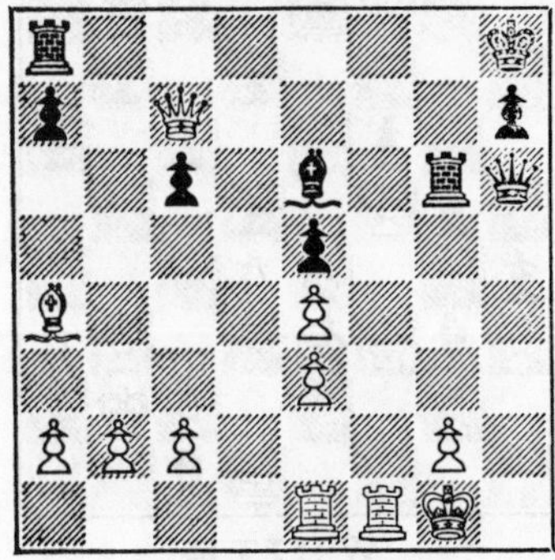

WHITE

Black moves

85. One move reduces Black to helplessness.
86. Black forces a won ending.
87. Again Black forces a won ending.
88. From a blindfold game won by Morphy.

89

BLACK

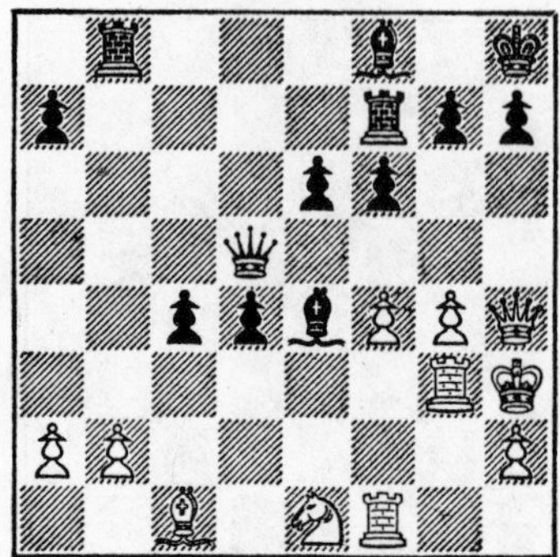

WHITE

Black moves

90

BLACK

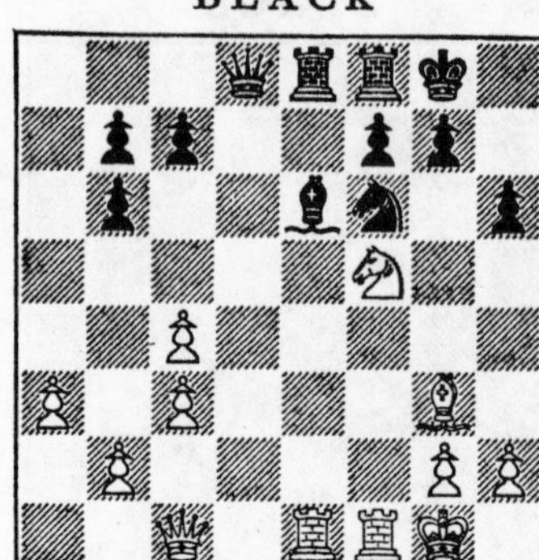

WHITE

White moves

91

BLACK

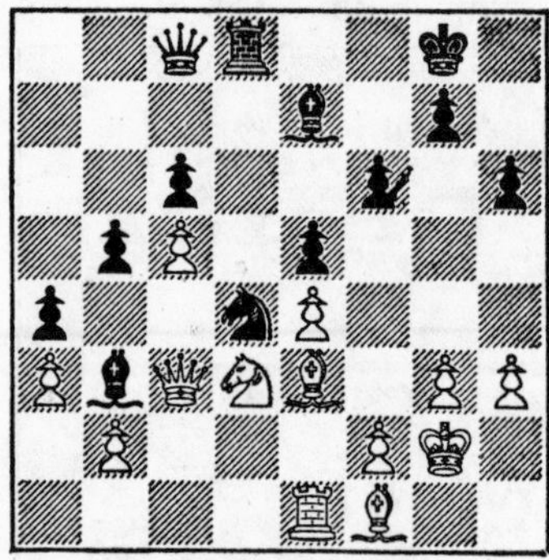

WHITE

Black moves

92

BLACK

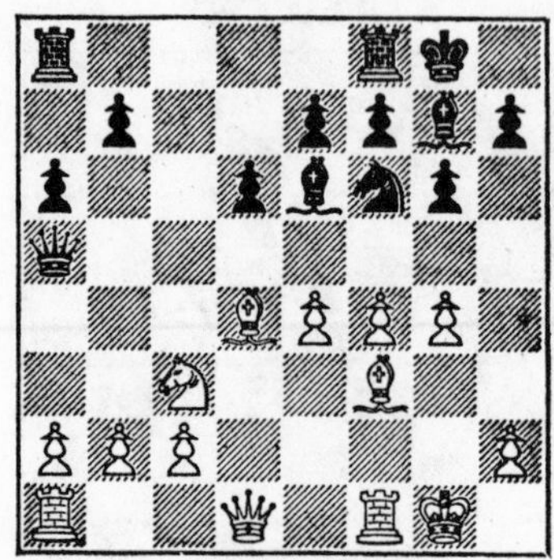

WHITE

Black moves

89. A defensive combination by Tarrasch.
90. The brilliant Tchigorin is the victim of a brilliant attack.
91. Black unerringly finds the weak spot.
92. Are there any weaknesses in White's position? Apparently not!

93

BLACK

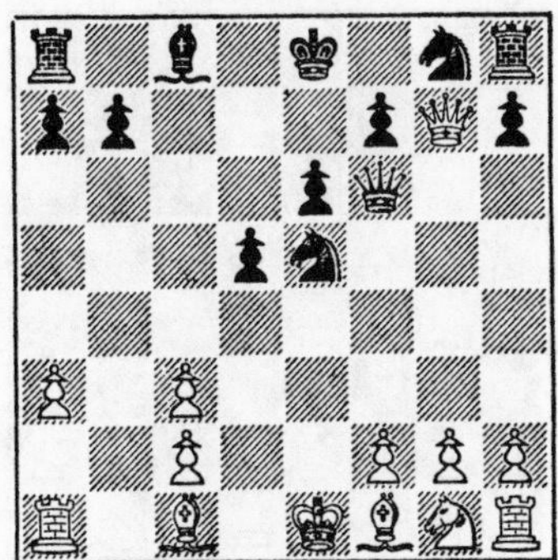

WHITE

White moves

94

BLACK

WHITE

Black moves

95

BLACK

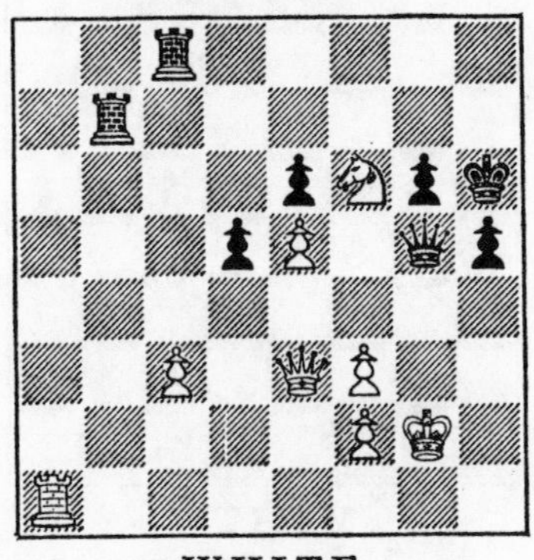

WHITE

White moves

96

BLACK

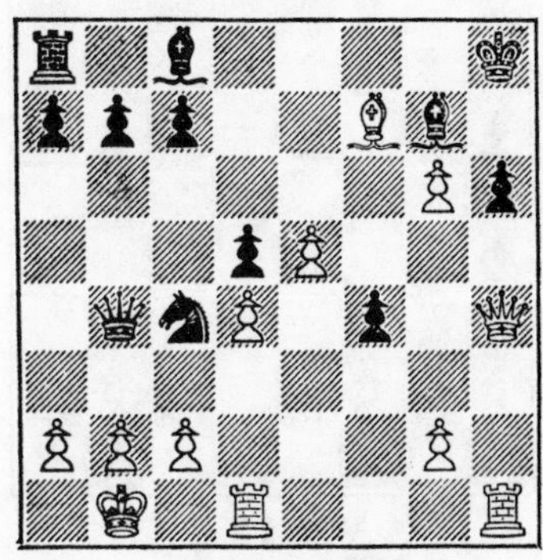

WHITE

White moves

93. How does White win the exchange?
94. Tarrasch wins artistically.
95. Has Black overlooked something?
96. Who mates first?

97

BLACK

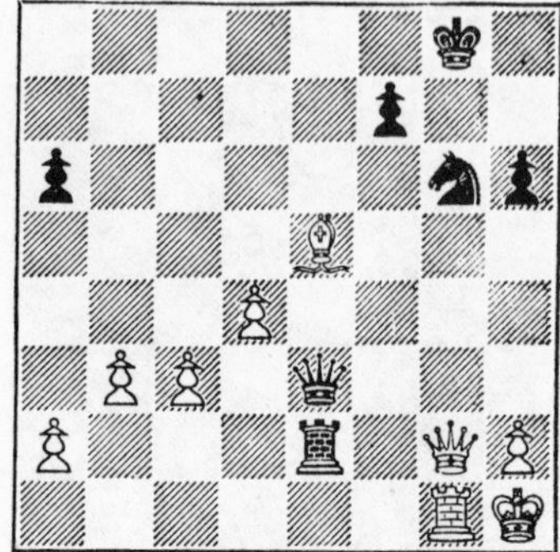

WHITE

White moves

98

BLACK

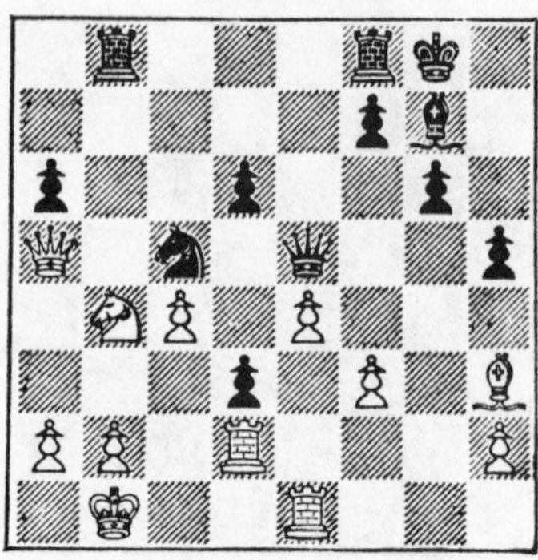

WHITE

Black moves

99

BLACK

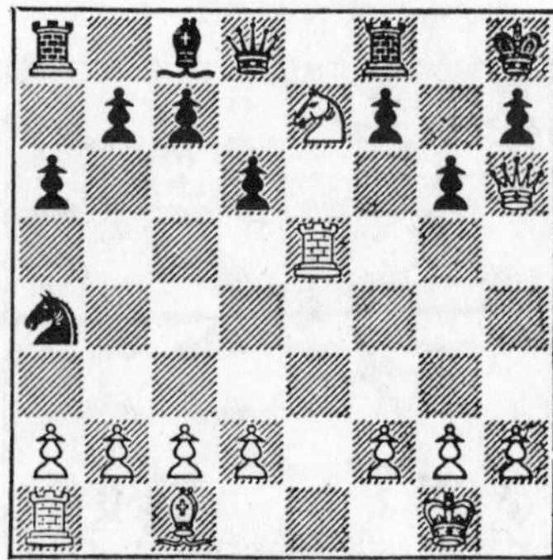

WHITE

White moves

100

BLACK

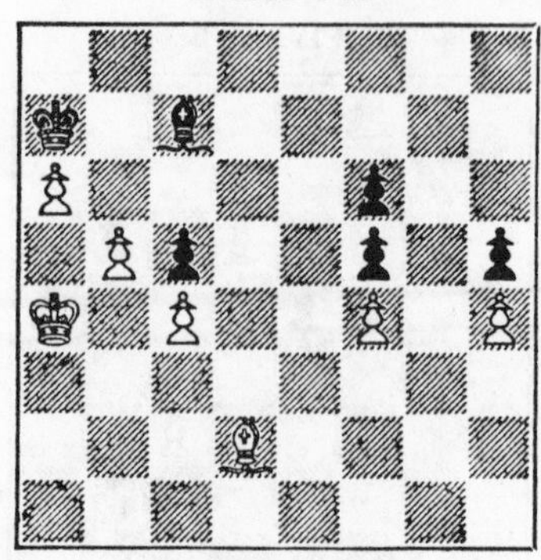

WHITE

White moves

97. White's attack is decisive.
98. Flohr has castled into a murderous attack. Tylor exploits his opportunity very cleverly.
99. The conclusion of an old but still enjoyable trap.
100. In actual play, Bird was unable to win this ending.

FIFTH QUIZ

81. White has sacrificed a piece in the expectation of regaining it advantageously. However, by playing *1* . . . B–Q3! *2* R×B, Kt–K1 Black comes out the exchange to the good.

82. White wins with *1* B–R7 *ch,* K–B1; *2* Q–R3 *ch,* R–K2; *3* B–Q3!

83. White's *1* Q×B! is immediately decisive.

84. The quickest way is *1* Q–Kt8 *ch!* R×Q; *2* Kt–B7 *mate.* A novel setting for a smothered mate.

85. *1* Kt–R6! leaves Black without a satisfactory defense. Black is punished for the unprotected state of his Queen.

86. Black wins with *1* . . . Kt–Kt5 *ch;* *2* Kt×Kt, RP×Kt followed by . . . P–R4! and eventually . . . P–Kt4 and . . . P–B5. With a passed RP and KBP he wins easily.

87. Black wins quickly with *1* . . . R×Kt! *2* P×R, P–Q5!

88. Black forces mate quickly with *1* . . . R×P *ch,* etc. Hardly surprising in view of the open file and White's lack of defensive resources.

89. Black wins a Rook by *1* . . . P–Kt4! *2* P×P (or *2* Q–R5, B–Kt3), P×P, etc.

90. White smashes up Black's King-side with *1* Kt×P, K×Kt; *2* B–K5.

91. Black exploits the weakness of White's King-side with *1* . . . B–K3! *2* P–KKt4, B×KtP; *3* P×B, Q×P *ch;* *4* K–R1, Kt–B6. *If 2* P–KR4, B–R6 *ch;* *3* K–R1, B×B; *4* R×B, Q–R6 *ch;* *5* K–Kt1, Kt–B6 *mate.*

92. Black unexpectedly snatches a Pawn with *1* . . .

Kt×KtP! for if *2* B×B (if *2* B×Kt, QB×B, etc), Q–R4! and Black avoids the loss of a piece.

93. White forces the win of the exchange with *1* B–KR6! (threat: Q×Q followed by B–Kt7). Note that Black cannot try to save himself with *1* . . . Kt–Kt5 because of *2* Q–B8 *ch,* K–Q2; *3* B–Kt5 *ch* with a mate in the offing.

94. The winning method is as simple as it is pretty. Black wins the Queen with *1* . . . P–K5 *ch! 2* K×P, Kt–B6 *ch* or *2* Q×P, Kt–B4 *ch.*

95. Black is under the impression that he is forcing the exchange of Queens with an easily won ending. Instead, he loses his Queen after *1* Kt–Kt4 *ch!* P×Kt; *2* R–R1 *ch.*

96. Black threatens mate on the move, but White's attack hits home first: *1* Q–Q8 *ch,* Q–B1; *2* R×P *ch!* B×R; *3* Q–B6 *ch!* Q–Kt2; *4* R–R1!! Q×Q; *5* P×Q and mate follows!

97. White can win on material alone, but there is a quicker way: *1* Q–R8 *ch,* K–R2; *2* Q–R8 *ch!* Kt×Q; *3* R–Kt7 *mate.*

98. *1* . . . Kt×P! or *1* . . . Kt–Kt6! forces White's resignation.

99. There is an elegant win with *1* R–KR5! P×R; *2* Q–B6 *mate.*

100. In actual play this ending was drawn! White wins with 1 P–Kt6 *ch!* K×KtP; *2* B–R5 *ch,* K–B3; *3* B×B, K×B; *4* K–Kt5 or *1* . . . B×P; *2* K–Kt5! and again White wins easily.

SIXTH QUIZ

101

BLACK

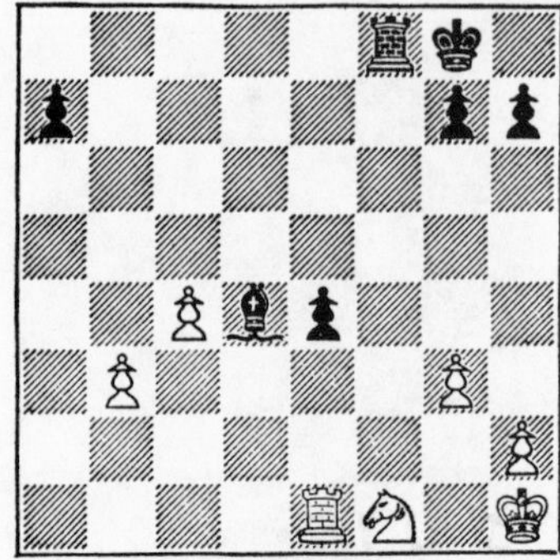

WHITE

Black moves

102

BLACK

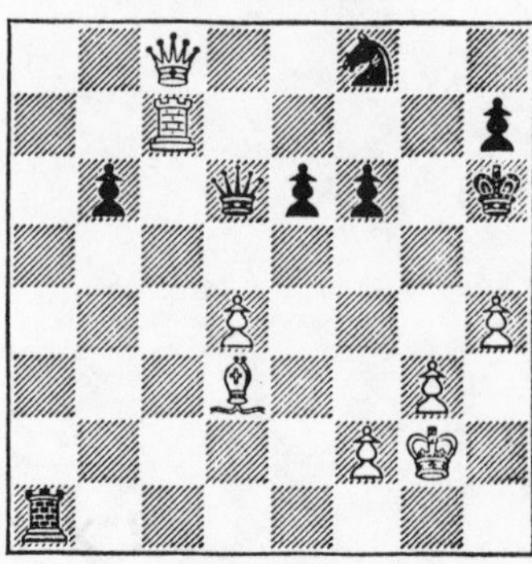

WHITE

White moves

103

BLACK

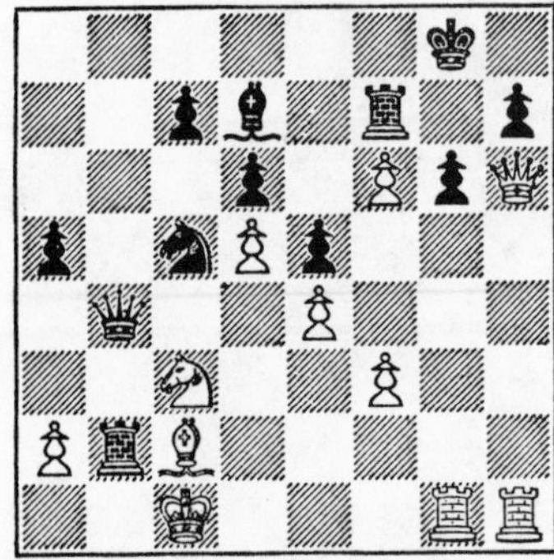

WHITE

White moves

104

BLACK

WHITE

White moves

101. Tarrasch puts the passed Pawn to good use.
102. From the 1921 World Championship Match.
103. White's attack hits home first.
104. Black's position on the long diagonal is shaky.

105

BLACK

WHITE

Black moves

106

BLACK

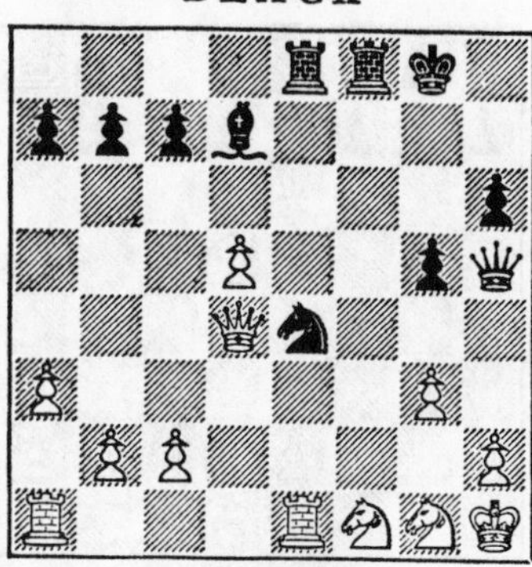

WHITE

Black moves

107

BLACK

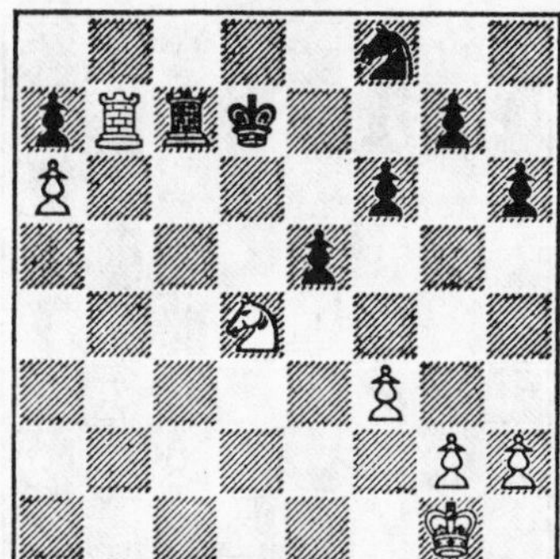

WHITE

White moves

108

BLACK

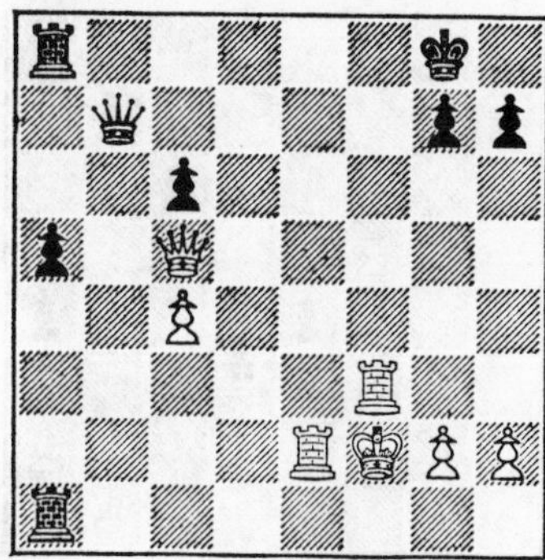

WHITE

White moves

105. The same comment applies, with colors reversed.

106. A neat Nimzovich combination.

107. White forces the win at once.

108. In this position, Tartakover overlooked the win of a Rook.

109

BLACK

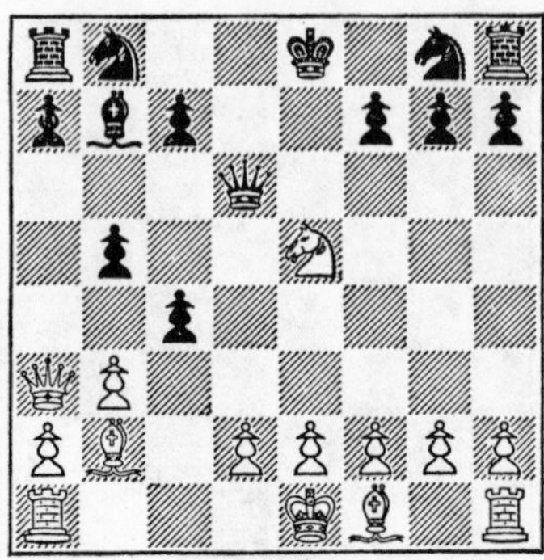

WHITE
Black moves

110

BLACK

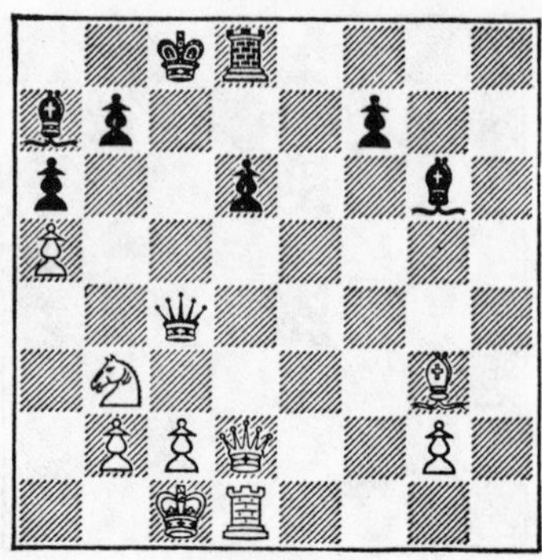

WHITE
Black moves

111

BLACK

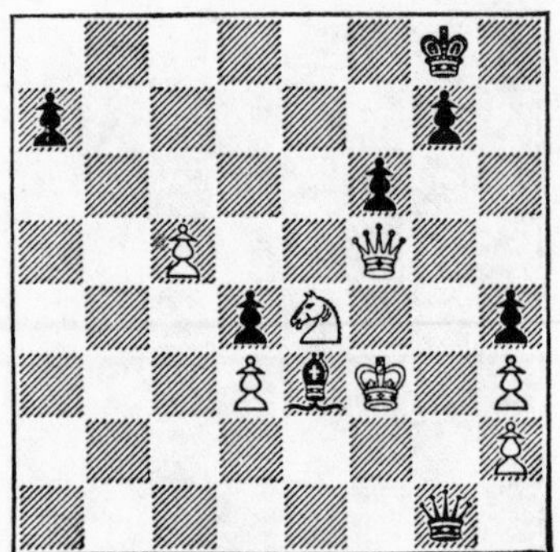

WHITE
Black moves

112

BLACK

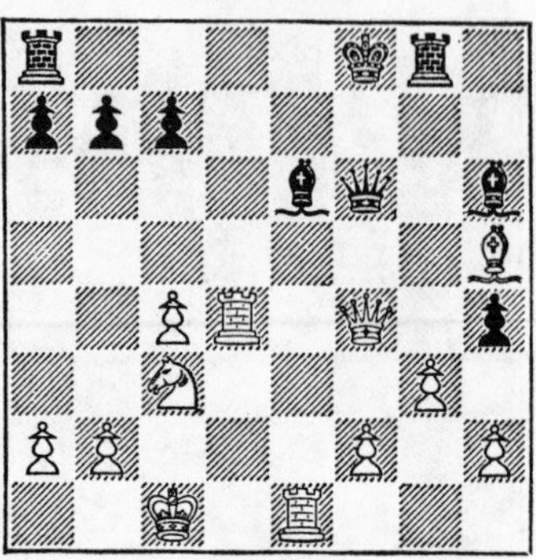

WHITE
White moves

109. Here Edward Lasker overlooked the win of a piece.

110. Rubinstein misses a decisive material gain.

111. Here Yates overlooked a forced win.

112. Even this desperate position has hidden resources!

113

BLACK

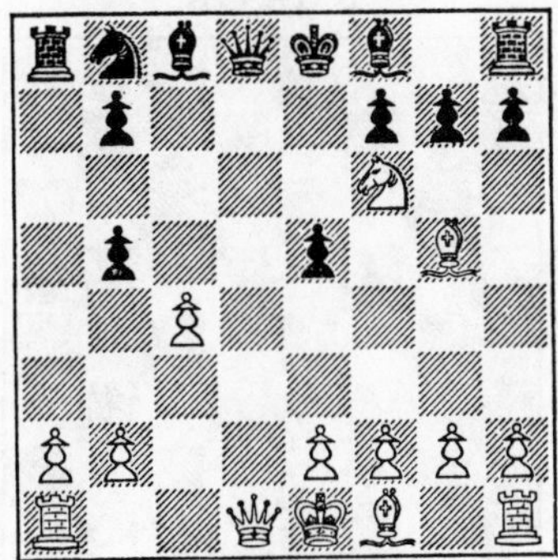

WHITE
Black moves

114

BLACK

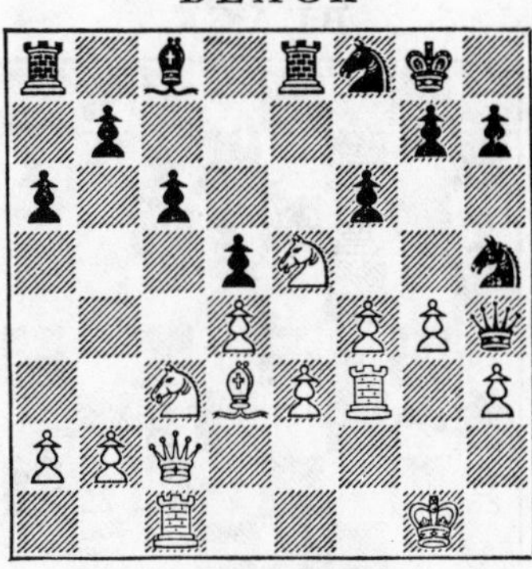

WHITE
White moves

115

BLACK

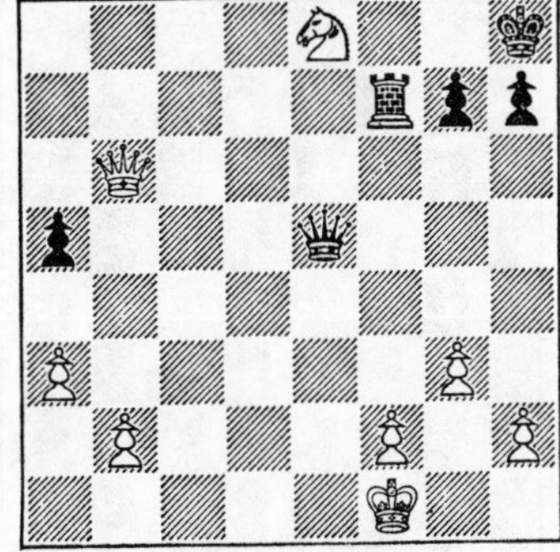

WHITE
White moves

116

BLACK

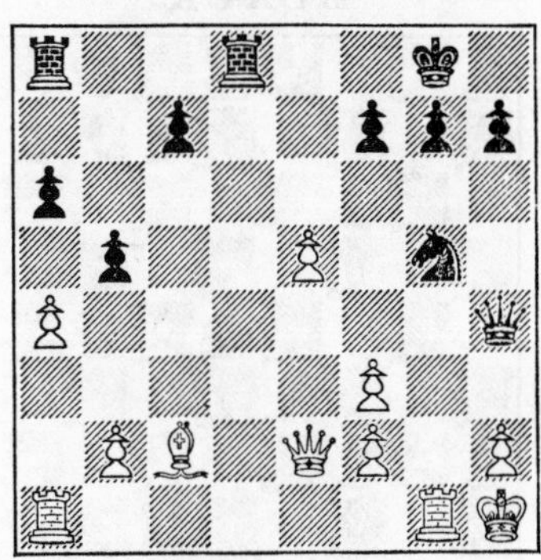

WHITE
Black moves

113. Can Black avoid the loss of a piece?

114. Black has overextended himself.

115. White has a decisive move.

116. What crushing move is at Black's disposal?

117

BLACK

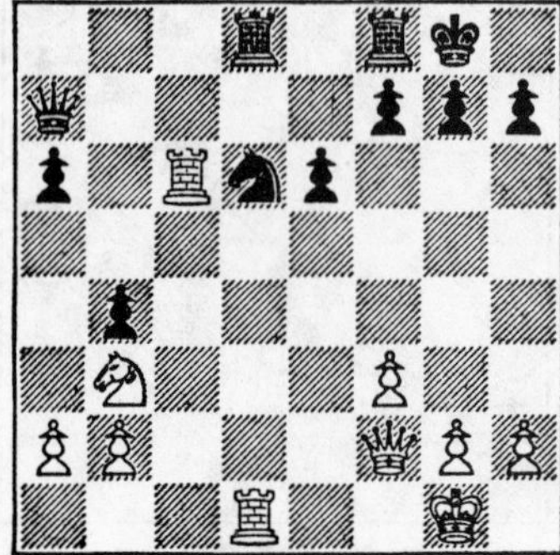

WHITE

Black moves

118

BLACK

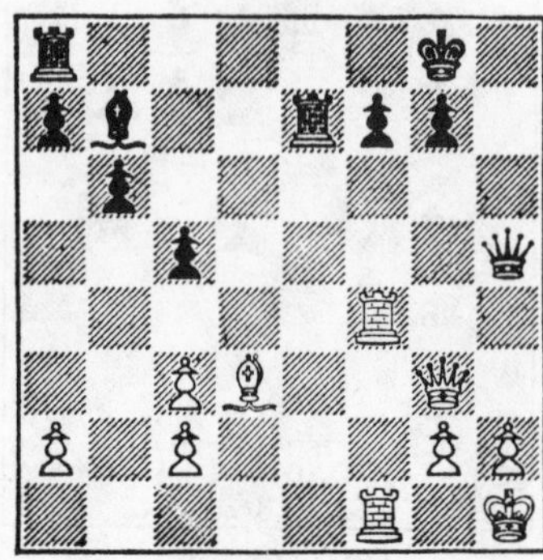

WHITE

White moves

119

BLACK

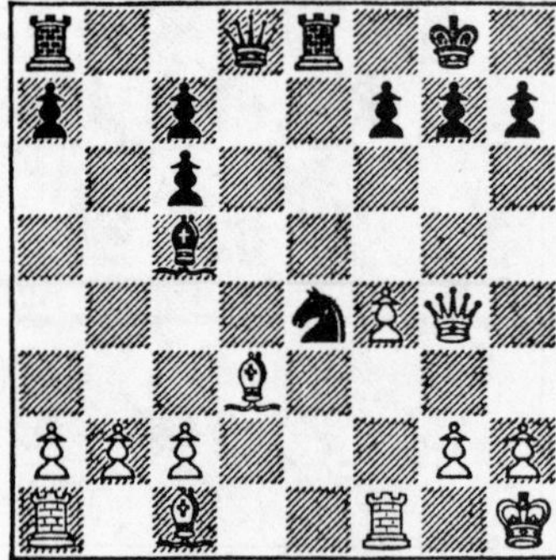

WHITE

Black moves

120

BLACK

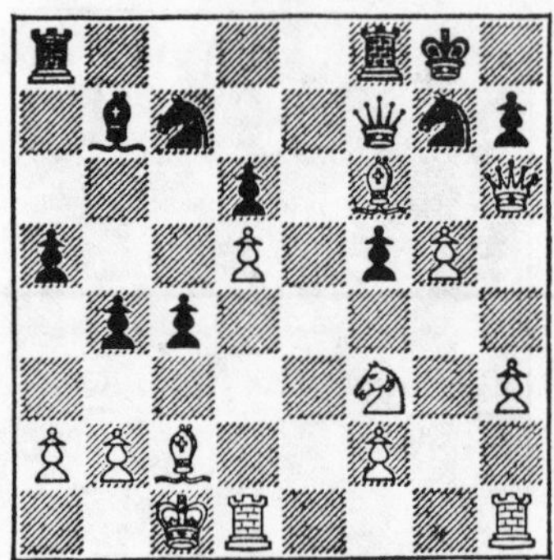

WHITE

White moves

117. Black decides the game at once.

118. White missed a forced win against Dr. Lasker!

119. What is Black's most effective continuation?

120. Steinitz has a curious winning move against Blackburne.

SIXTH QUIZ

101. Black wins with *1* . . . B—B6! *2* R—B1, R×Kt *ch;* *3* R×R, P—K6. Note that *1* . . . R×Kt *ch?* *2* R×R, P—K6; *3* R—K1 would lose for Black.

102. White forces a neat mate with *1* Q×Kt *ch!* Q×Q; *2* R×P *mate.*

103. There is a quick mate with *1* Q×KtP *ch,* etc.

104. White wins a piece with *1* Q×Kt! for if *1* . . . Kt×Q; *2* Kt×P *mate.*

105. *1* . . . Q×P! is decisive; if *2* P×Q, B—R7 *mate.* Black's magnificent attacking position, coupled with White's lack of defensive facilities, spells disaster for White.

106. Black concludes neatly with *1* . . . Kt—B7 *ch;* *2* K—Kt2, B—R6 *ch;* *3* Kt×B, Q—B6 *ch;* *4* K—Kt1, Kt×Kt *mate* or *4* . . . Q—R8 *mate.*

107. White wins with *1* Kt—Kt5 as Black cannot play *1* . . . R×R? because of *2* P×R and the Pawn queens!

108. White wins a Rook with *1* Q—K5! attacking the loose Rook and threatening mate with Q—K8 *ch,* etc.

109. Black missed an opportunity to win a piece here with *1* . . . P—B6! A curious position.

110. In this position, Black could have won White's Queen with *1* . . . B—K6!

111. Black accepted a draw here, although he could have won with *1* . . . Q—B8 *ch;* *2* K—Kt4, Q—K7 *ch;* *3* K×P (or *3* Q—B3, P—B4 *ch*), P—Kt4 *ch;* *4* K—Kt3, B—B5 *ch.*

112. White's Queen is lost because of the pin by the Bishop, but he wins by means of a counter-pin: *1* R×B, B×Q *ch;* *2* R×B, etc.

113. Black wins a piece with *1* . . . Q×Kt! (not 1 . . . P×Kt? 2 Q×Q *ch,* K×Q; 3 B×P *ch*); 2 B×Q, B—Kt5 *ch,* etc. A terrible surprise for White!

114. White wins the Queen in curious fashion: *1* B×P *ch!* Kt×B; *2* Kt—Kt6. Black's Queen had ventured too far afield.

115. White takes advantage of Black's unprotected first rank to play *1* Kt—Q6! Q—B3 (if 1 . . . R—B1; 2 Kt—B7 *ch!*); 2 Kt×R *ch,* Q×Kt; *3* Q—Q8 *ch* winning easily.

116. Black wins a piece with *1* . . .R—Q7! for if *2* Q×R, Kt×P simultaneously threatening mate and attacking the Queen.

117. Black wins with the beautiful move *1* . . . Kt—K5! Another example of the inadequately protected first rank.

118. White missed the following rather easy win: *1* R—KR4, Q—K4; *2* R—R8 *ch!* K×R; *3* Q—R4 *ch,* K—Kt1; *4* Q—R7 *ch,* K—B1; *5* Q—R8 *mate.*

119. Black wins a piece with *1* . . . Q×B! *2* P×Q, Kt—B7 *ch.* Another example of the inadequately protected first rank.

120. White forces the win of a piece by *1* P—Kt6! Q×KtP (if 1 . . . P×P; 2 Kt—Kt5 wins); *2* B×Kt and Black cannot capture the Bishop because of R—Kt1.

SEVENTH QUIZ

121

BLACK

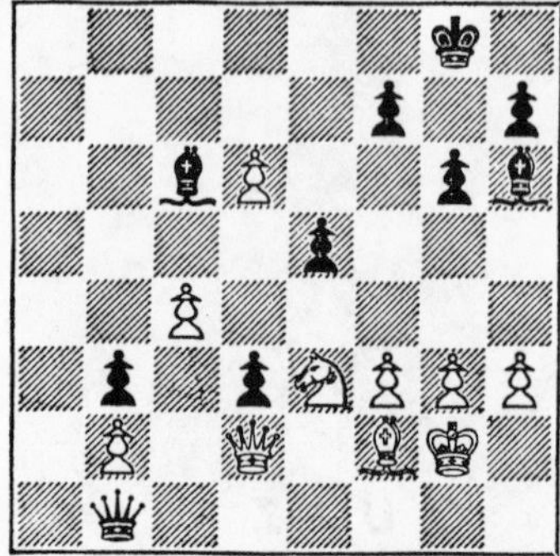

WHITE

Black moves

122

BLACK

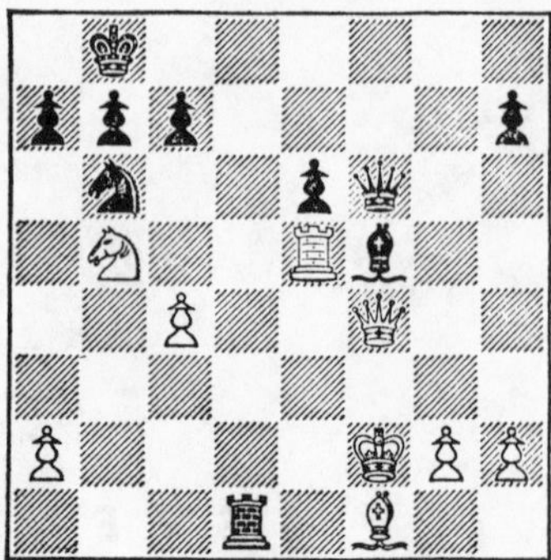

WHITE

Black moves

123

BLACK

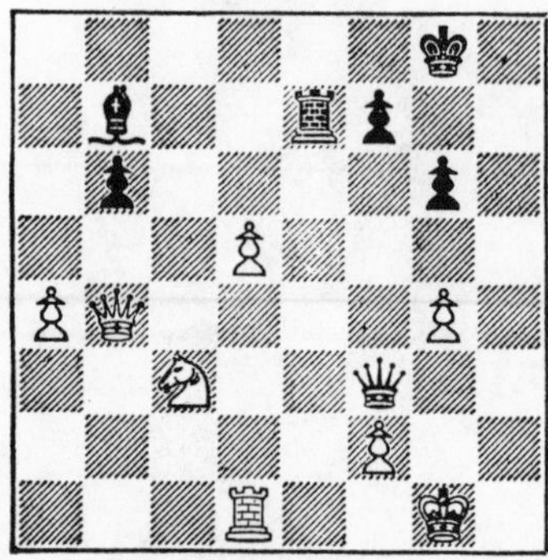

WHITE

Black moves

124

BLACK

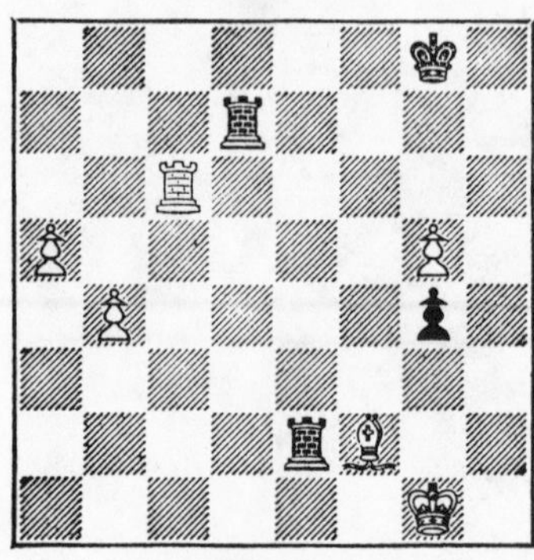

WHITE

Black moves

121. Black forces a quick win.

122. Euwe puts his finger on the weak spot in White's game.

123. The best defense is attack.

124. The Rooks are irresistible. Prove this in the quickest way.

125

BLACK

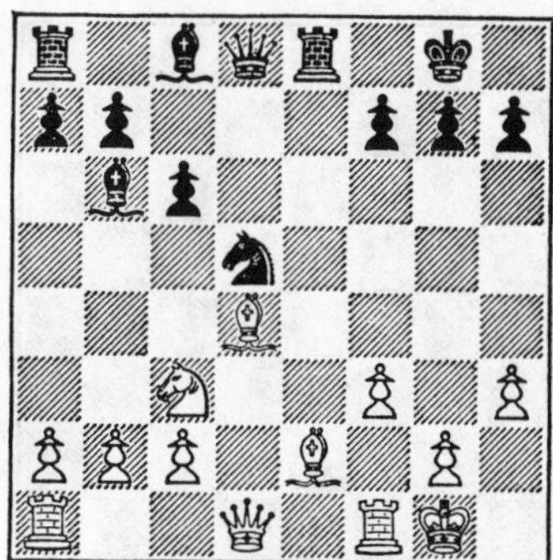

WHITE
Black moves

126

BLACK

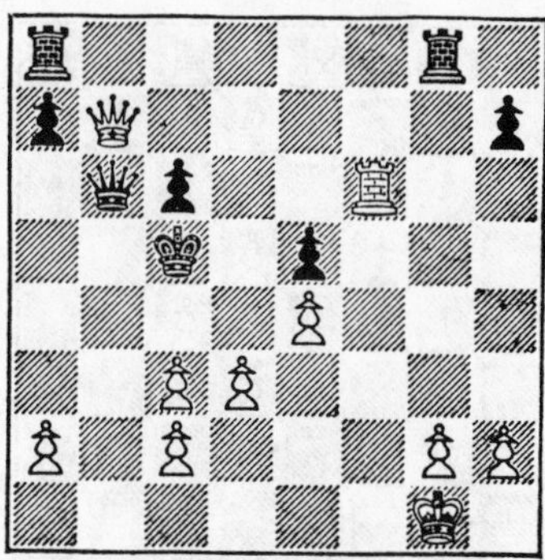

WHITE
White moves

127

BLACK

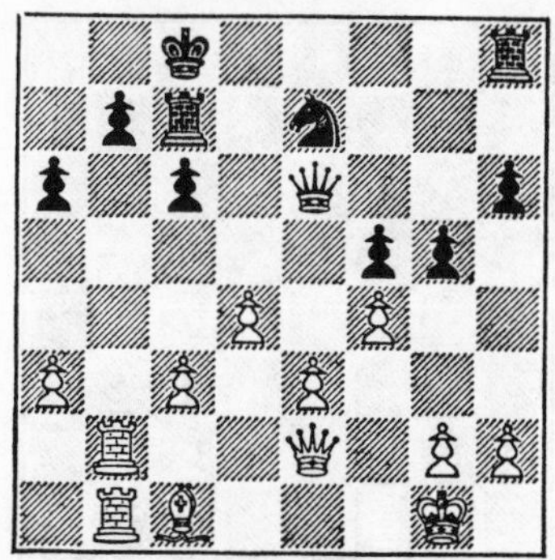

WHITE
White moves

128

BLACK

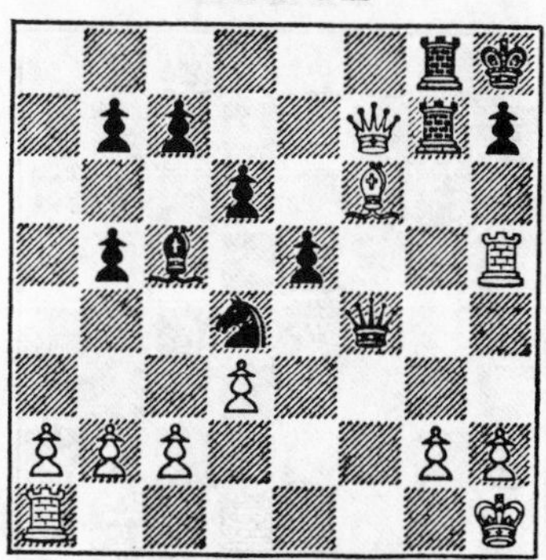

WHITE
White moves

125. White's position has a terrible weakness.
126. Black's material superiority is meaningless.
127. Black's King is vulnerable.
128. White cleverly utilizes the pinning motif.

129

BLACK

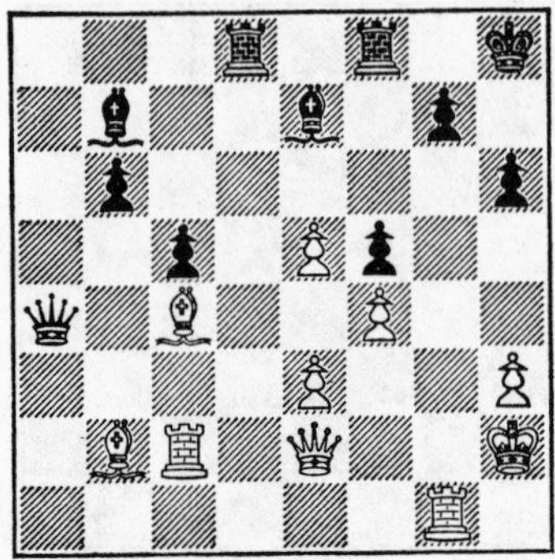

WHITE
Black moves

130

BLACK

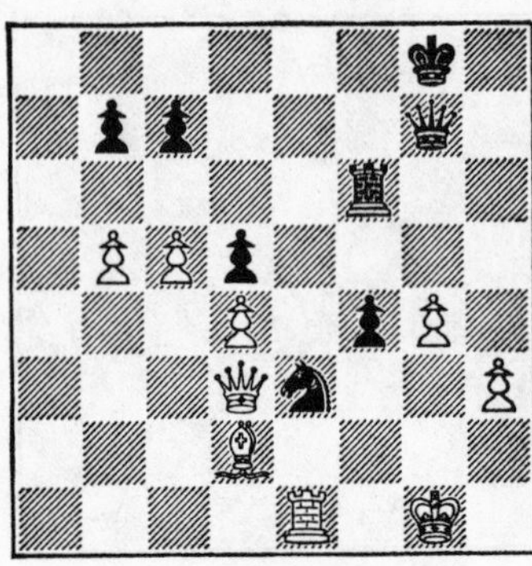

WHITE
Black moves

131

BLACK

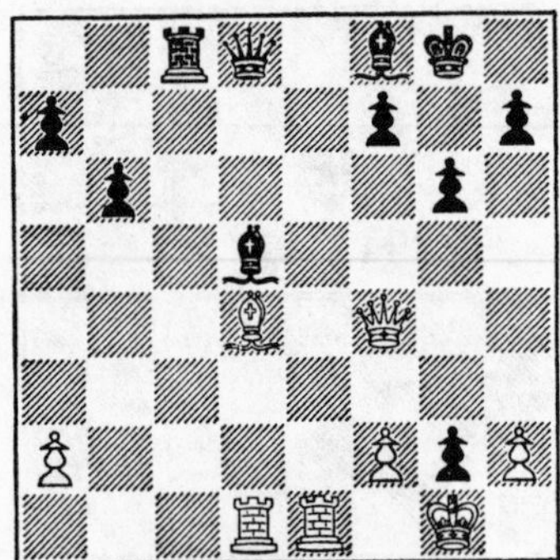

WHITE
White moves

132

BLACK

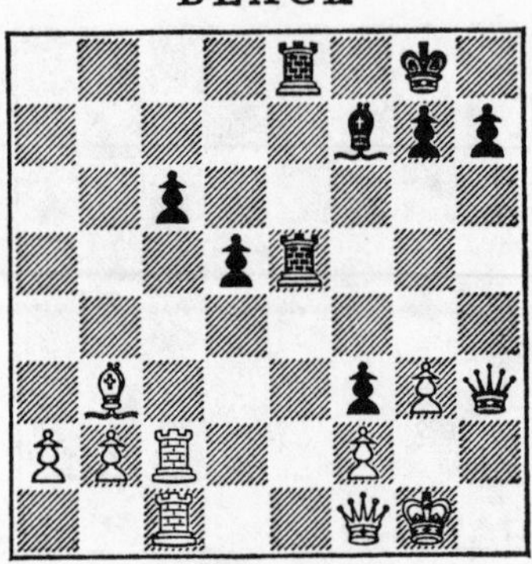

WHITE
Black moves

129. Black's Bishops are dynamite.
130. Black has a crushing move.
131. Atkins finds a neat diversionary maneuver.
132. There is a mate in the offing.

133

BLACK

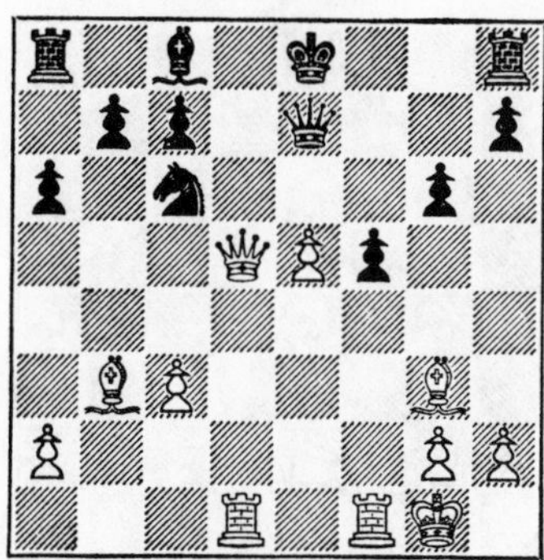

WHITE

White moves

134

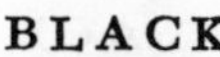

BLACK

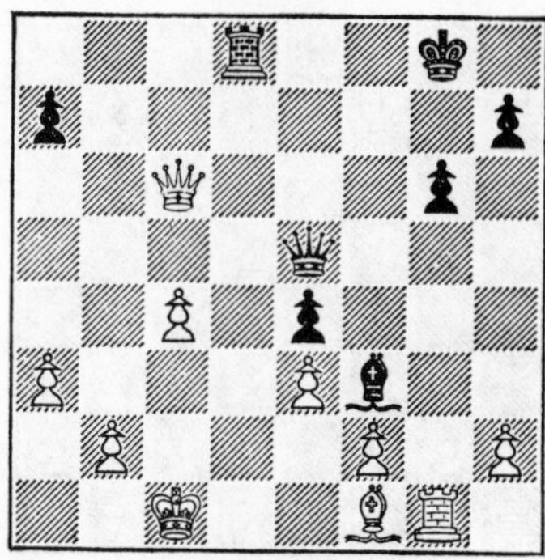

WHITE

Black moves

135

BLACK

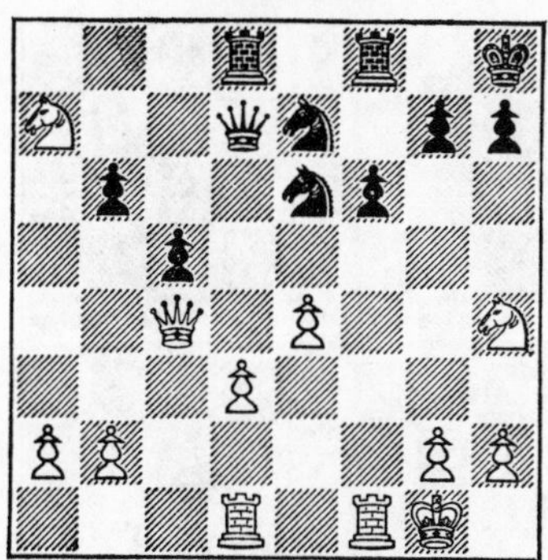

WHITE

Black moves

136

BLACK

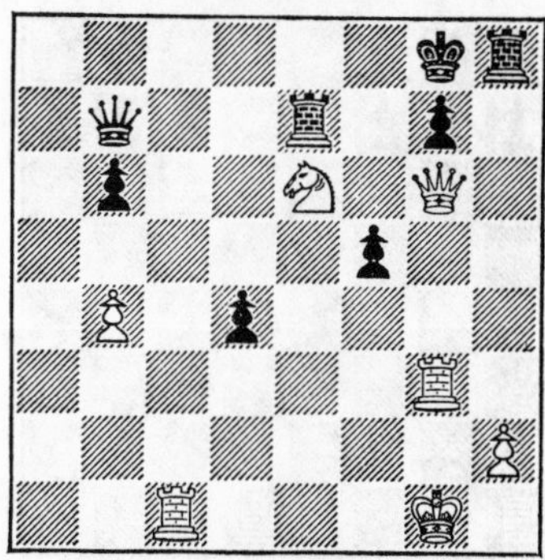

WHITE

White moves

133. Black's Queen is overburdened.

134. White's pieces are poorly placed for defensive purposes.

135. White's Knight has ventured too far to QR7.

136. White's position can stand a few sacrifices. His play is inspired!

137

BLACK

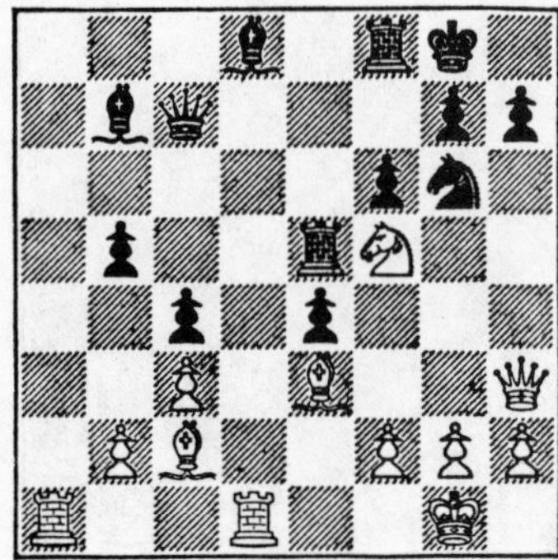

WHITE

White moves

138

BLACK

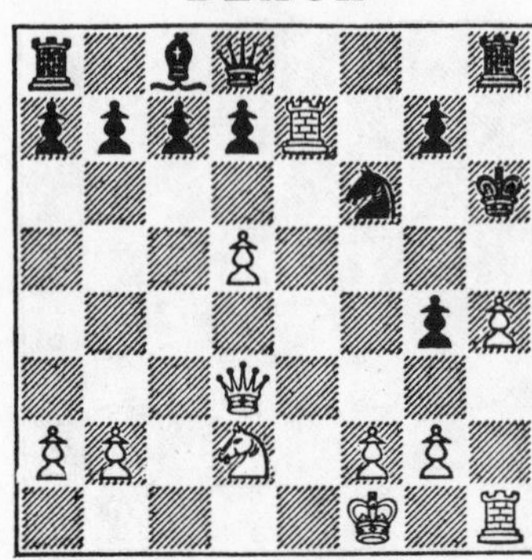

WHITE

White moves

139

BLACK

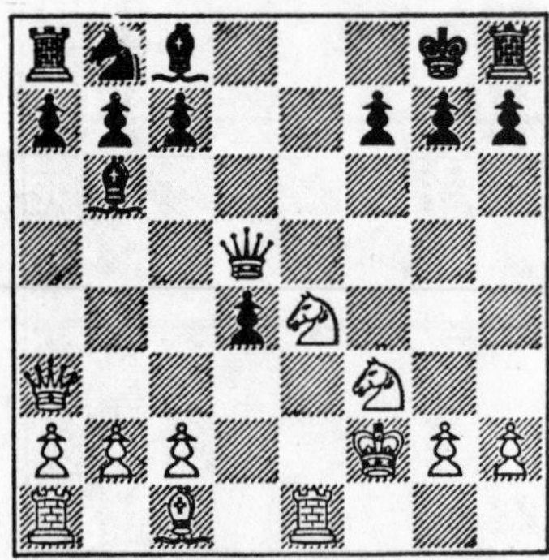

WHITE

White moves

140

BLACK

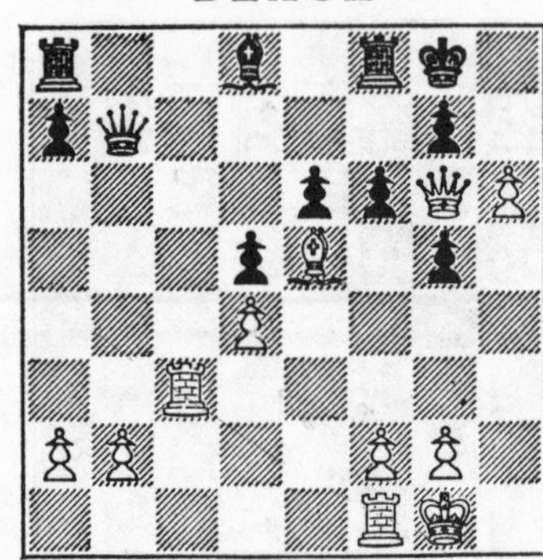

WHITE

White moves

137. Blackburne decides the game in brilliant style against Steinitz.

138. A dashing Marshall combination.

139. White's superior development is decisive.

140. White cuts his opponent's lines of communication.

SEVENTH QUIZ

121. Black wins with *1 . . .* B×P *ch!* *2* K×B, Q–R8 *ch* and if *3* K–Kt4, Q–K5 *mate.*

122. Black wins the Queen with *1 . . .* R×B *ch!* *2* K×R, B–Q6 *ch.*

123. Black's Rook is en prise, but he wins by putting another piece en prise: *1 . . .* B×P!

124. Black wins neatly with *1 . . .* P–Kt6! as the Bishop cannot move.

125. Black wins a piece in this apparently harmless position with *1 . . .* B×B *ch!* *2* Q×B, Kt×Kt; *3* Q×Q, Kt×B *ch.* White failed to reckon with the interpolated check.

126. White winds up a brilliant attack with *1* R×P *ch!* Q×R; *2* Q–Kt4 *mate.*

127. White wins with *1* R×P, R×R; *2* Q×P, Q–Q2; *3* Q–R8 *ch,* etc.

128. *1* Q–Kt6! (double pin!) leaves Black nothing better than giving up the Queen with *1 . . .* Q×B.

129. Black's Bishops assert themselves with *1 . . .* B–B6! *2* Q–B2, B–R5! winning at least the exchange.

130. Black has a winning move in *1 . . .* Q–R3! If for example 2 K–R2, Q×P *ch!* 3 K×Q, R–R3 *mate!*

131. White forces the game with *1* R–K8! Q×R; *2* Q–B6. Black's Queen was overburdened.

132. Black forces through his attack with *1 . . .* R–K8! *2* R×R, R×R. White suffers from a combination of an inadequately protected first rank and an overburdened Queen.

133. *1* B–KR4! leaves Black without a satisfactory reply:

1 . . . Q–Kt2; *2* Q–Q8 *ch!* Kt×Q; *3* R×Kt *mate.* Again a case of an overburdened Queen.

134. Black has a quick mate with *1* . . . R–Q8 *ch;* 2 K–B2, R–Q7 *ch!* White's forces are scattered and he has indulged in injudicious Pawn-grabbing.

135. Black plays *1* . . . Kt–Q5! (naturally not 1 . . . Q×Kt; 2 Q×Kt) and the venturesome Knight is trapped.

136. White wins incisively with *1* R–B8 *ch!* Q×R; *2* Q×P *ch!* R×Q; *3* R×R *mate.* Again an overburdened Queen and inadequate protection of the last rank.

137. *1* R–Q7! Q×R; *2* Kt–R6 *ch* wins the Queen.

138. White wins with *1* P–R5! Kt×P; *2* Q–B5, P–KKt3; *3* R×Kt *ch,* P×R; *4* Q–B6 *mate.* The combination of an exposed King and poor development was more than Black's position could stand.

139. There is a neat mate in four with *1* Kt–B6 *ch!* P×Kt; *2* Q–B8 *ch!* K×Q; *3* B–R6 *ch,* K–Kt1; *4* R–K8 *mate.* Black's lack of development tells the story.

140. White wins prettily with *1* R–B7! cutting off the Black Queen's protection of the King-side.

EIGHTH QUIZ

141

BLACK

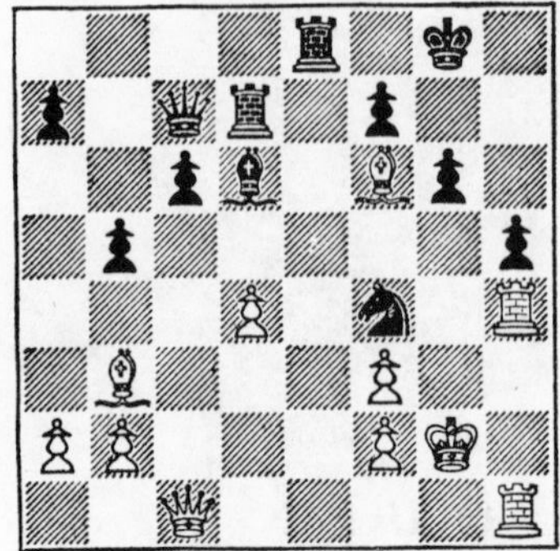

WHITE

White moves

142

BLACK

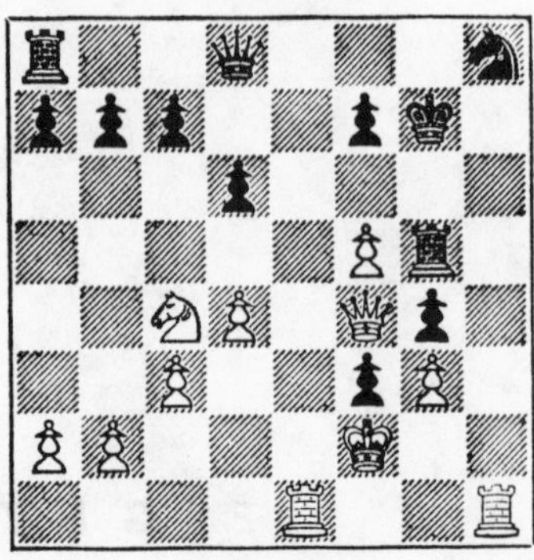

WHITE

White moves

143

BLACK

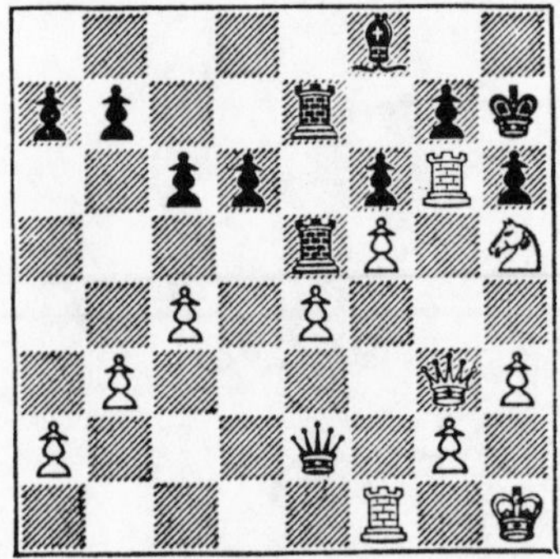

WHITE

White moves

144

BLACK

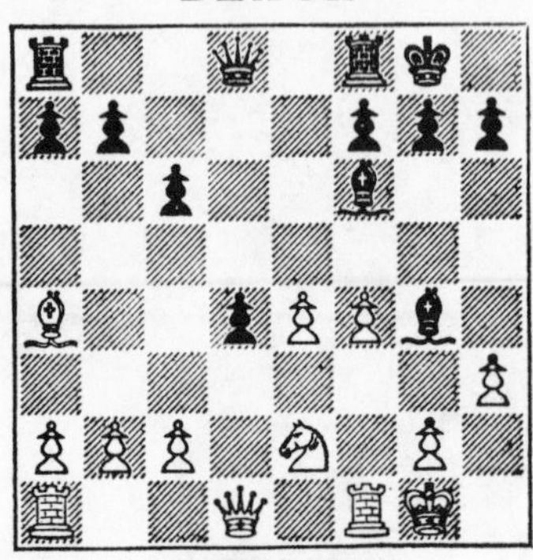

WHITE

Black moves

141. Blackburne's most famous combination.

142. White (Tchigorin) has two winning methods.

143. Dr. Lasker forces an elegant win.

144. What is Black's best move?

145

BLACK

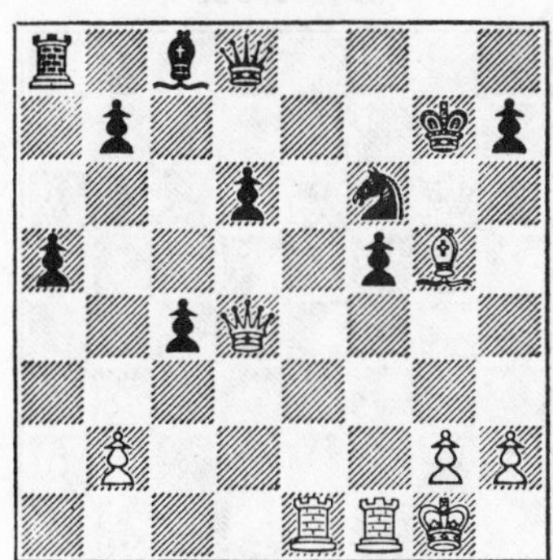

WHITE

White moves

146

BLACK

WHITE

White moves

147

BLACK

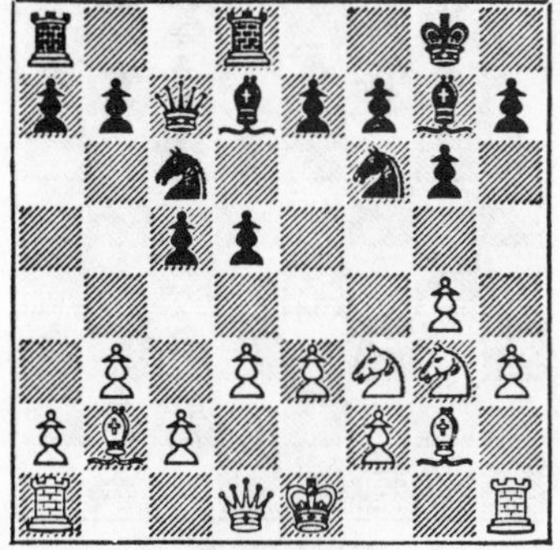

WHITE

Black moves

148

BLACK

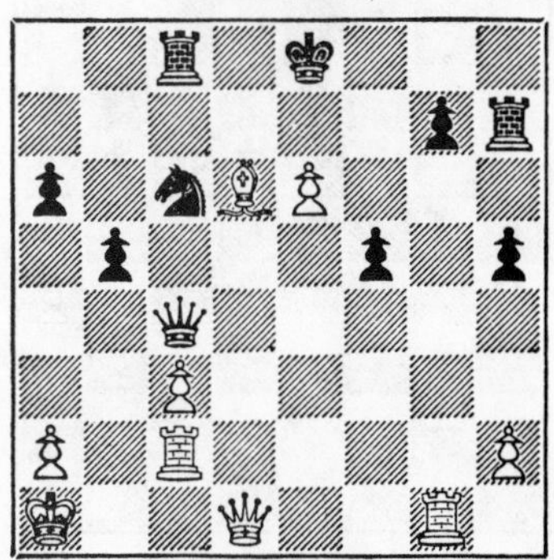

WHITE

White moves

145. Nimzovich drives away the hostile Queen.

146. The winning method is not easy to find.

147. From a game that made Miss Menchik famous.

148. A Tchigorin gem. His KP is important.

149

BLACK

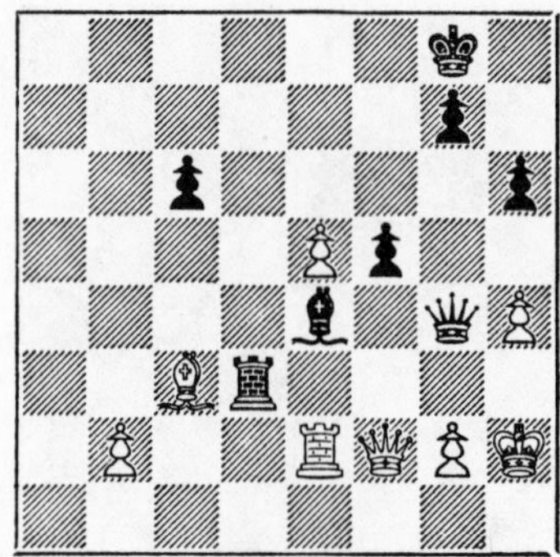

WHITE

Black moves

150

BLACK

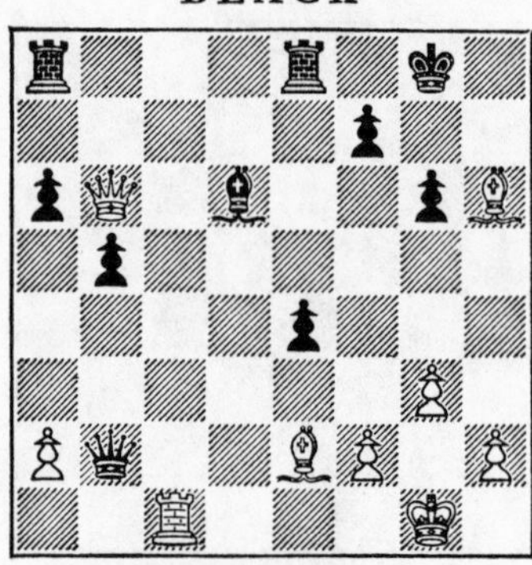

WHITE

Black moves

151

BLACK

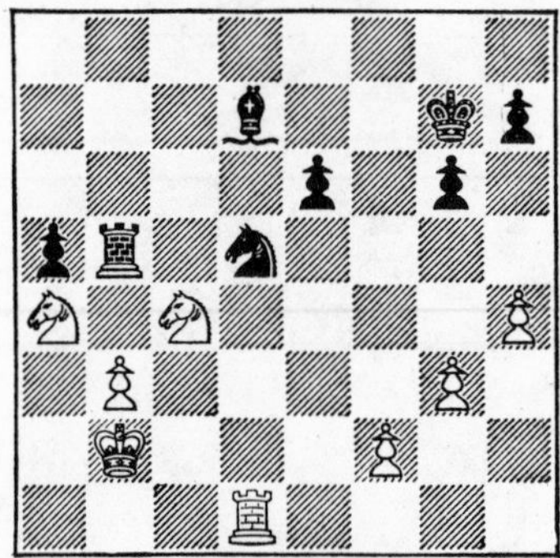

WHITE

White moves

152

BLACK

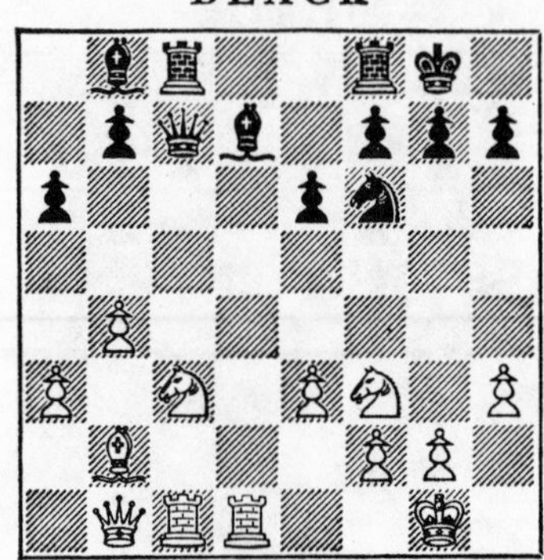

WHITE

White moves

149. White's position is ripe for demolition.
150. Black has an amusing and crushing move—but not too obvious!
151. Capablanca demonstrates the power of the Knight.
152. The position of Black's Queen is precarious.

153

BLACK

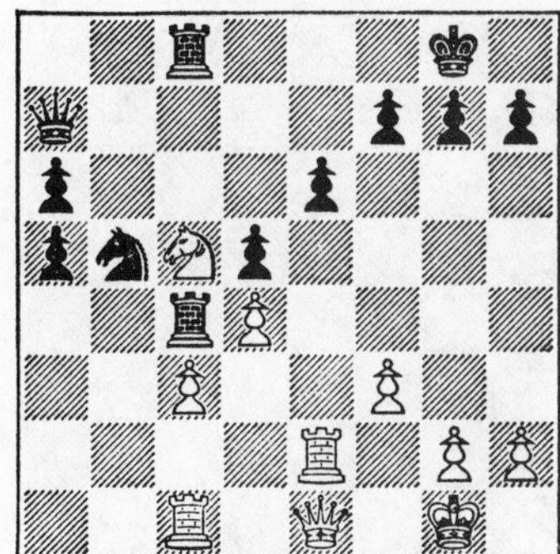

WHITE

Black moves

154

BLACK

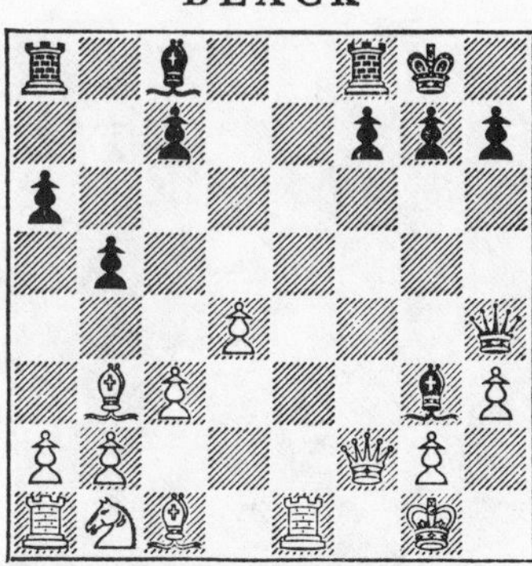

WHITE

White moves

155

BLACK

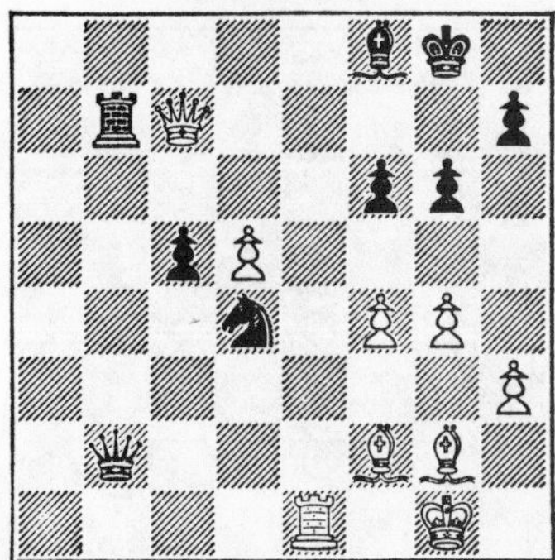

WHITE

White moves

156

BLACK

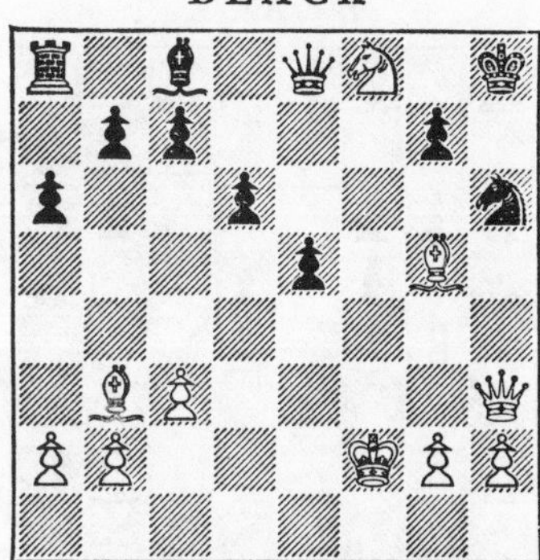

WHITE

White moves

153. Capablanca smashes up White's position.

154. Can White save his Rook? Apparently there is no hope for him.

155. Naidorf has a surprising winning method.

156. White's Queen plays an important part in the attack.

157

BLACK

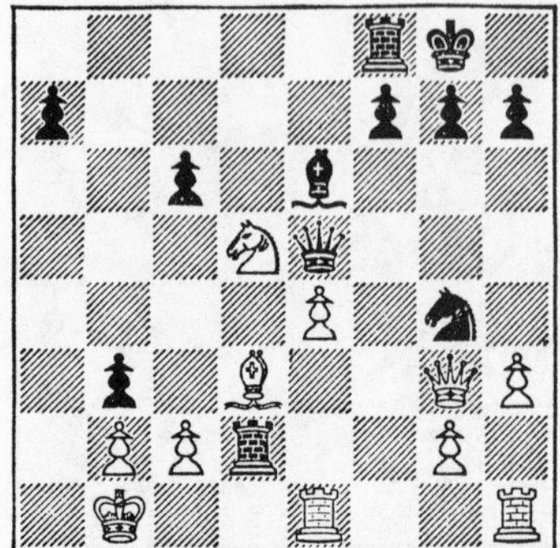

WHITE

White moves

158

BLACK

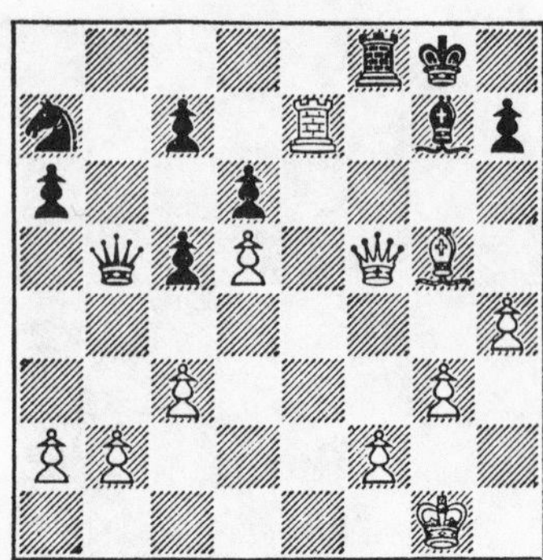

WHITE

White moves

159

BLACK

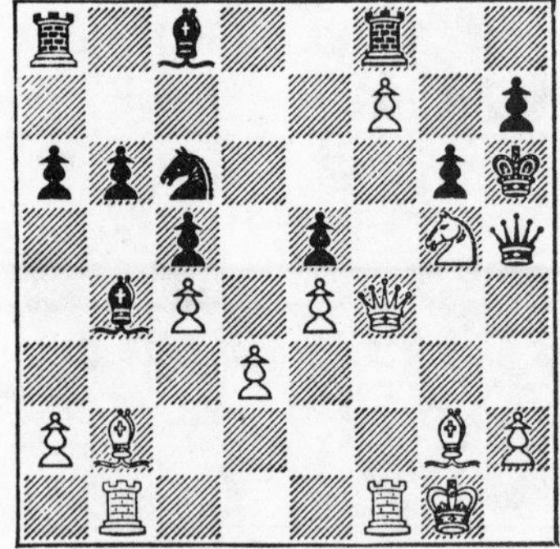

WHITE

White moves

160

BLACK

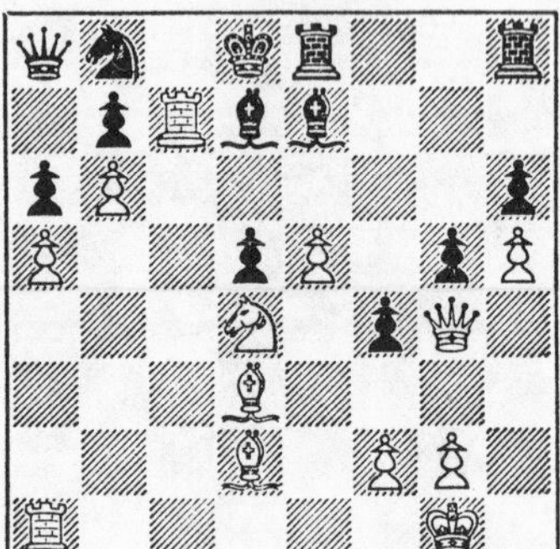

WHITE

White moves

157. White wins a piece.
158. Black's pieces are poorly placed for defensive purposes. White's combination sparkles!
159. Can White save his threatened Knight?
160. An example of Nimzovich's ability to tie up his opponent's pieces.

EIGHTH QUIZ

141. A famous Blackburne finish: *1* Q×Kt! B×Q; *2* R×P! P×R; *3* R×P and Black cannot stop mate.

142. The quickest win is *1* R—K8! Black suffers from not having his pieces developed fully or harmoniously.

143. Black's pieces are unfortunately posted for defensive purposes, so that White winds up drastically with *1* R×RP *ch!* K—Kt1 (or 1 . . . P×R; 2 Kt×P *ch,* K—R1; 3 Q—Kt8 *mate*); *2* Kt×P *ch,* K—B2; *3* Q—Kt6 *mate.*

144. Black wins a piece neatly with *1. . .* P—Q6! *2* P×B (if 2 Q×P, Q×Q, etc. and if 2 P×P, B×Kt; 3 Q×B, Q—Q5 *ch,* etc.), P×Kt; *3* Q×P (if 3 Q×Q, P×R(Q) *ch*), Q—Q5 *ch.* The unprotected position of White's Bishop has been neatly exploited.

145. White wins by attacking the overburdened Queen: *1* R—K8! Q×R; *2* Q×Kt *ch,* K—Kt1; *3* B—R6 and it is all over.

146. At first sight this one is a puzzler, for if 1 B—Q3, K—K6; 2 B—B1, K—B7; 3 B—R3, K—Kt6; 4 B—B5, K—B5; with similar doings after 1 B—R3, K—Kt6, etc. The win: *1* B—B8! P—B7 (other moves are answered by P—B5 followed by B—R6); *2* B—R3, K—Kt6; *3* B—B1 and wins.

147. Black wins at least a Pawn with *1 . . .* Kt×P! for if *2* B×B, Kt×P, etc. When Bishops face each other along a masked diagonal, there is always some danger involved for the unprotected Bishop.

148. *1* R×P! is decisive. If *1 . . .* R—KR1; *2* Q×P *ch!* leads to mate.

149. Black wins with *1 . . .* B×P! *2* Q×B, Q×P *ch; 3* K—Kt1, R—Kt6, etc.

150. Black is already the exchange ahead, and wins more

material with *1* . . . B—B1! No matter how White replies, he must lose a piece.

151. White (Capablanca) forces the win of a Pawn by a charming maneuver: *1* Kt—B3, R—B4; *2* Kt—K4; R—Kt4; *3* Kt(K4)—Q6, R—B4; *4* Kt—Kt7, R—Kt4; *5* Kt(7)×P.

152. It is always risky to have one's Queen on the same file with a hostile Rook, as Black soon discovers to his sorrow: *1* Kt—Q5! Q—Q1; *2* R×R! wins the Queen (2 . . . B×R; 3 Kt×Kt *ch* or 2 . . . Q×R; 3 Kt—K7 *ch*).

153. White, by playing P—KB3, has somewhat weakened the diagonal leading to his King. Black exploits this weakness in masterly style by playing *1* . . . Kt×QP! 2 P×Kt, R(1)×Kt! with an easy win (if 4 P×R, Q×P *ch* and White can resign).

154. Going in for a headlong attack, Black has overlooked the murderous counter of *1* Q×P *ch!* R×Q; *2* R—K8 *mate.* Again the unprotected first rank leads to catastrophe.

155. Instead of retreating his Queen, White simply plays *1* P—Q6! leaving Black helpless.

156. White has an unconventional mate in *1* Q×Kt *ch!* P×Q; 2 B—B6 *mate.*

157. White wins prettily with *1* P×Kt! for if *1* . . . Q×Q; 2 Kt—K7 *ch,* K—R1; *3* R×P *ch!* etc.

158. White has sacrificed a piece for the following finish: *1* R×B *ch!* K×R; 2 B—R6 *ch!* K×B; *3* Q—Kt5 *mate.*

159. A typically original Nimzovich finish: *1* Kt—K6 *ch!* P×Q (else a Rook is lost); 2 B—Kt7 *mate!*

160. Black has allowed himself to be tied up in knots and succumbs to the following appropriate conclusion: *1* Q×B *ch!* Kt×Q; 2 Kt—K6 *mate!*

NINTH QUIZ

161

BLACK

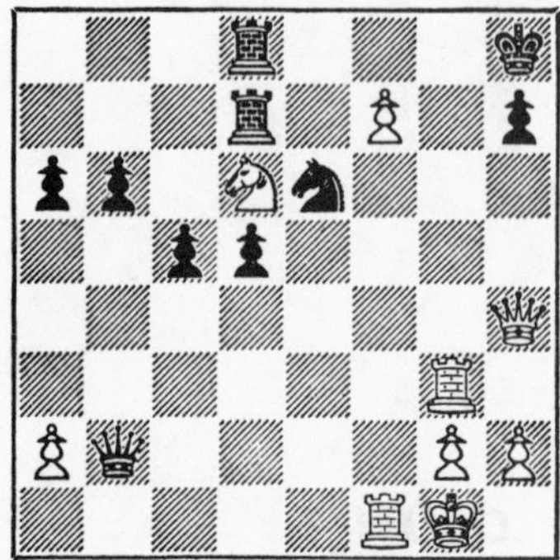

WHITE
White moves

162

BLACK

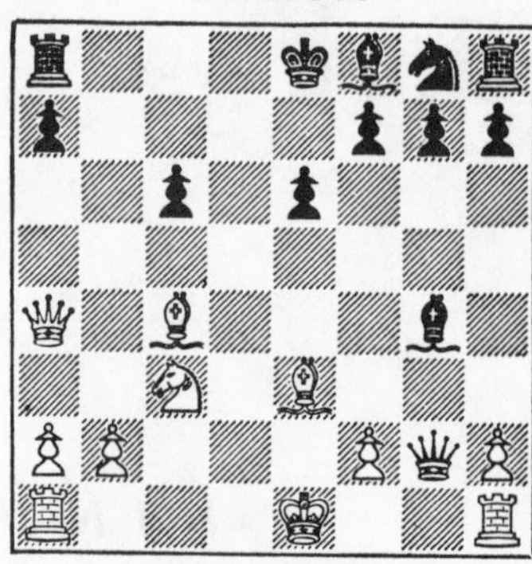

WHITE
White moves

163

BLACK

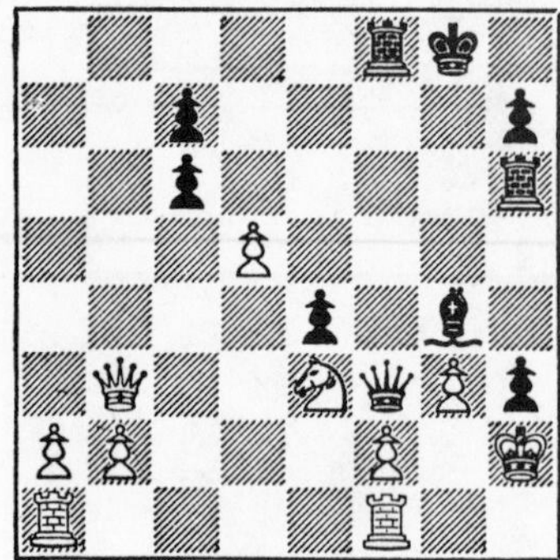

WHITE
Black moves

164

BLACK

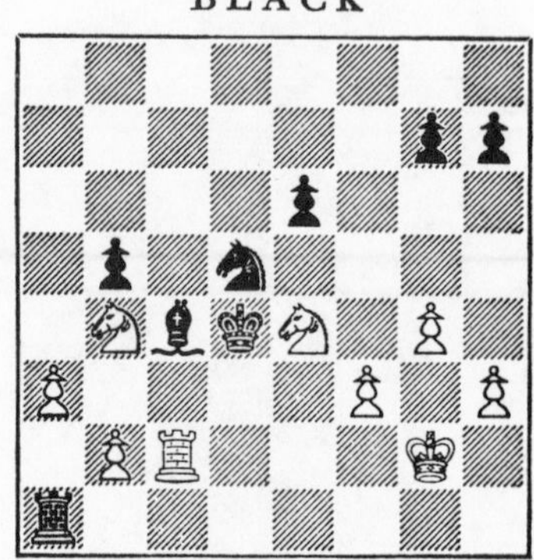

WHITE
White moves

161. How does White utilize the promotion theme?
162. Again attack is the best defense.
163. Black has a forced mate.
164. White's Knights are agile in the hands of a wizard like Lasker.

165

BLACK

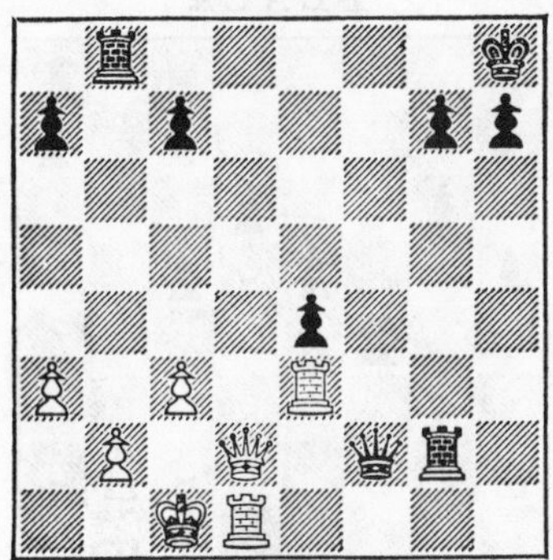

WHITE

White moves

166

BLACK

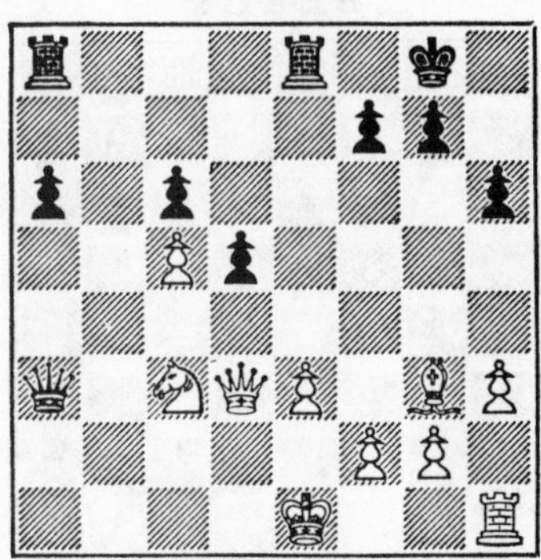

WHITE

Black moves

167

BLACK

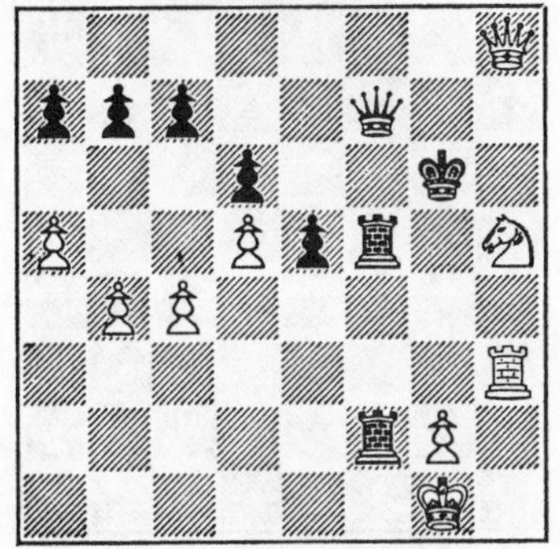

WHITE

Black moves

168

BLACK

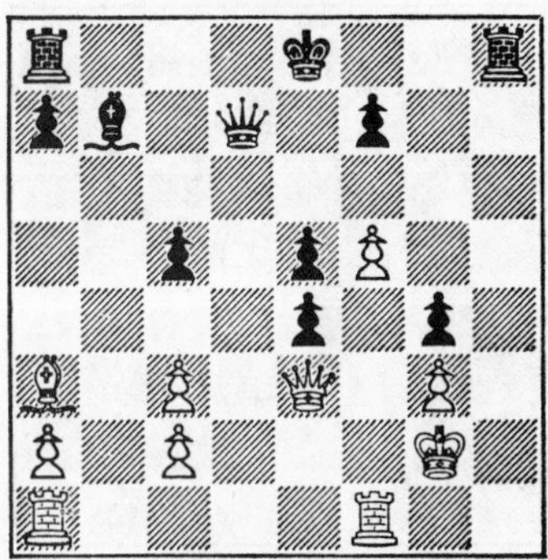

WHITE

Black moves

165. Black's first rank is vulnerable—but how?
166. Black wins a piece. Find the quickest way.
167. Black seizes the attack.
168. Black bludgeons his opponent into submission.

169

BLACK

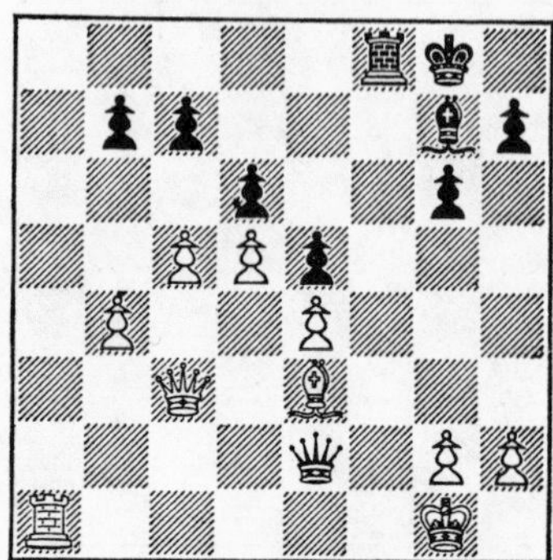

WHITE

Black moves

170

BLACK

WHITE

White moves

171

BLACK

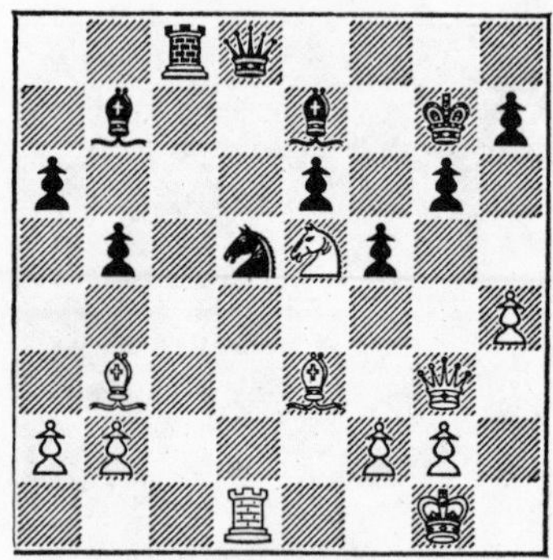

WHITE

White moves

172

BLACK

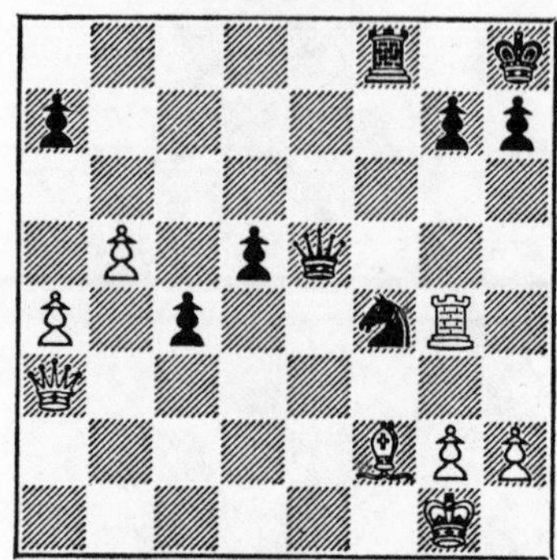

WHITE

Black moves

169. White's forces are deflected from the defense.
170. The discovered check is the key to the win.
171. Black's position is riddled with weaknesses.
172. White's forces are scattered, but the smashing finish is surprising.

173

BLACK

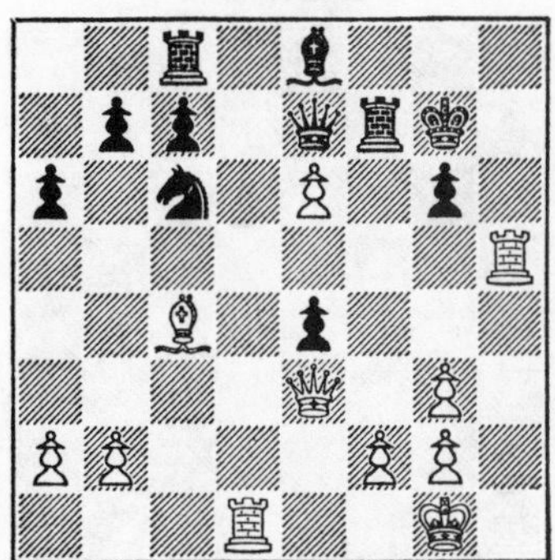

WHITE

White moves

174

BLACK

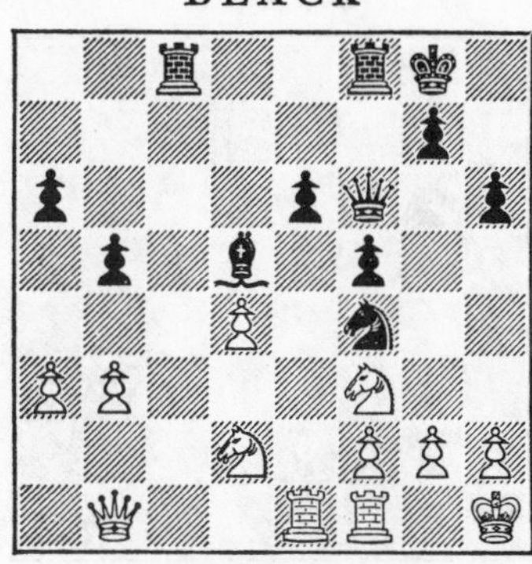

WHITE

Black moves

175

BLACK

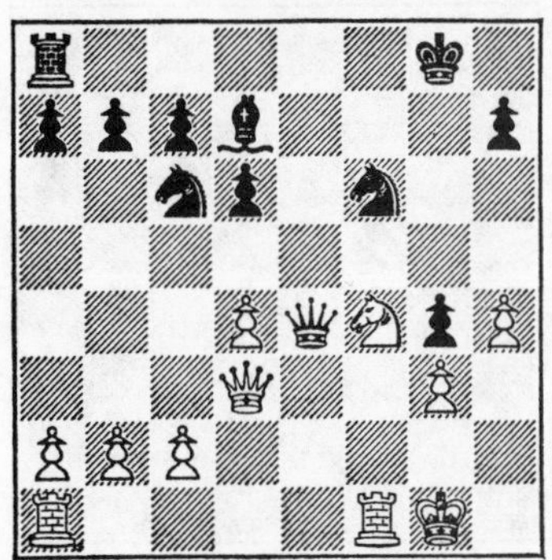

WHITE

White moves

176

BLACK

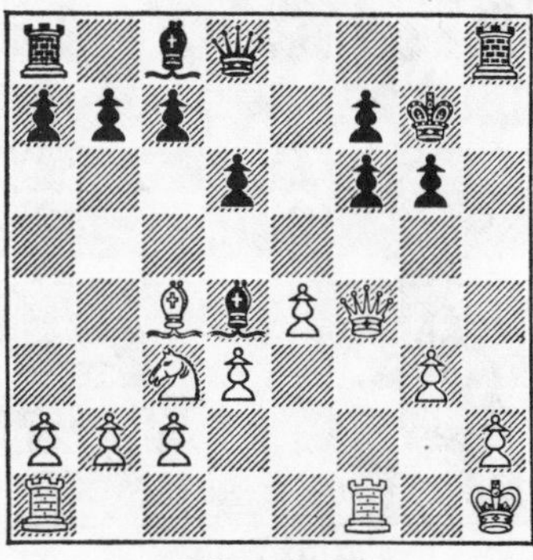

WHITE

Black moves

173. Black's King is too insecure.

174. Black's Bishop is an interested spectator.

175. Steinitz wins a piece.

176. The KR file proves useful. White's previous play has been careless.

177

BLACK

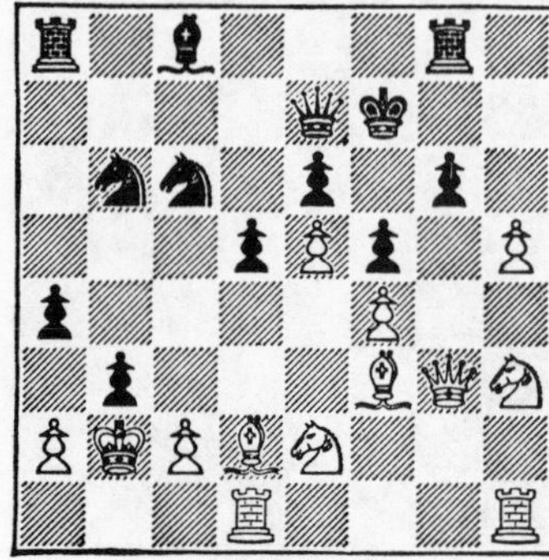

WHITE

Black moves

178

BLACK

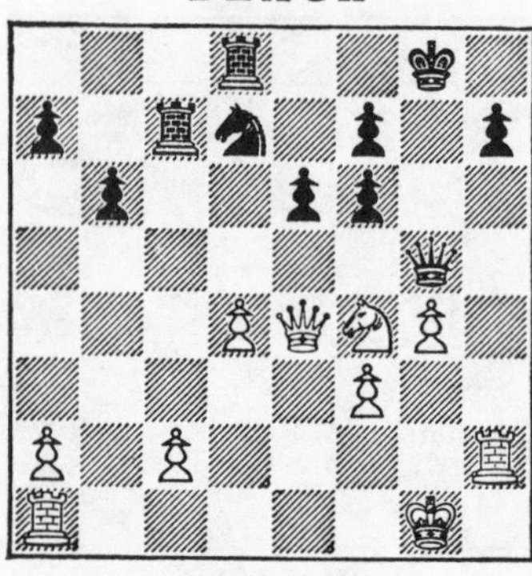

WHITE

White moves

179

BLACK

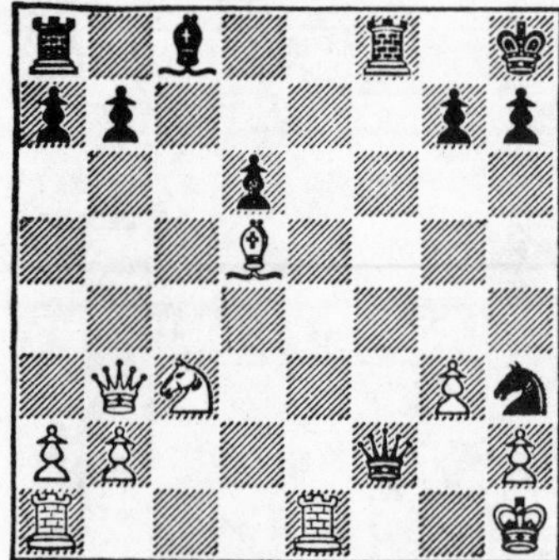

WHITE

Black moves

180

BLACK

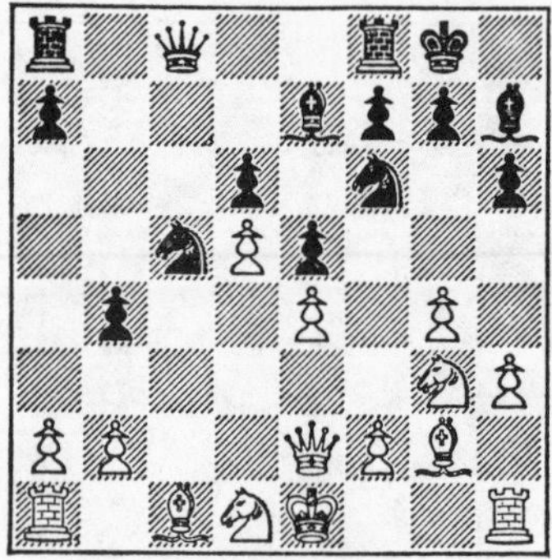

WHITE

Black moves

177. Black's attack hits home first.

178. White wins—but not in the most obvious way! Bernstein at his best.

179. A Blackburne blindfold brilliancy.

180. Reti breaks through in what is apparently a blocked position.

NINTH QUIZ

161. Black has gone Pawn-hunting, exposing himself to the following fine finish: *1* Q×R *ch!* R×Q; *2* P–B8(Q) *ch,* R×Q; *3* R×R *ch,* Kt×R; *4* Kt–B7 *mate.*

162. Both players are in danger, but White has the first word with *1* B–Q5! which gives him a winning attack.

163. Black wins (and against Marshall!) with *1 . . .* Q–Kt7 *ch!! 2* Kt×Q, P×Kt *ch; 3* K×P (or 3 K–Kt1, B–B6), B–B6 *ch;* 4 Q×B, P×Q *ch; 5* K–Kt1, R–B4 followed by . . . R(4)–R4 and mate.

164. White comes out a piece ahead with the ingenious combination *1* R×B *ch!* K×R (if 1 . . . P×R; 2 Kt–B2 *ch*); *2* Kt–Q2 *ch* followed by *3* Kt–Kt3 *ch.*

165. Black appears to have an easy win (if 1 Q–Q8 *ch,* Q–B1). However, the unexpected *1* R–K2!! is at once decisive. Black loses because of his inadequately protected first rank.

166. The surprise move *1 . . .* P–Q5! wins a piece, for if *2* Q×QP, Q–R8 *ch,* etc.

167. Despite his exchange to the good, Black appears to be in some distress. However, he has a neat way out with *1 . . .* R×P *ch! 2* K×R, R–B7 *ch; 3* K–Kt3, Q–B6 *ch; 4* K–R4, Q–K5 *ch* and mate follows.

168. The game has barely left the opening stage, but Black has a forced win with the thunderbolt *1 . . .* Q–Q7 *ch!!* which leaves White without any resource. Beware of unmasked discovered checks!

169. It is no wonder that in this position, apparently so barren of tactical possibilities, that two such players as Euwe and Flohr overlooked the following forced win: *1 . . .* B–R3!! *2* R–K1 (if 2 B×B, Q–B7 *ch* and mate in two),

B×B *ch; 3* Q×B, R—B8 *ch!* winning the Queen. Another case of inadequately protected first rank.

170. The deadly discovered check cannot function directly because of . . . Kt×B. The difficulty is easily solved with *1* Q×Kt!

171. White quickly demolishes his opponent's weakened King-side with *1* B—R6 *ch!* K—Kt1; *2* Kt×P, etc.

172. Still another example of inadequately protected first rank: *1* . . . Q—K8 *ch! 2* B×Q, Kt—K7 *ch; 3* K—R1, R—B8 *mate.*

173. White has sacrificed a piece for an attack which succeeds quickly because Black's pieces are not properly posted for defensive purposes: *1* Q—R6 *ch,* K—B3; *2* R—B5 *ch!* K×R; *3* Q—B4 *mate.*

174. Black demonstrates the power of the menacing Bishop with *1* . . . Kt×P! *2* K×Kt, Q—Kt4 *ch; 3* K—R1, Q×Kt winning easily.

175. *1* Kt—R5! wins a piece.

176. Black makes the open KR file tell with *1* . . . R×P *ch! 2* K×R, P—KKt4! *3* Q—B5 (else . . . Q—R1 *ch* forces mate), B×Q, etc.

177. Black's attack comes through first: *1* . . . Q—R6 *ch!! 2* K×Q, Kt—B5 *mate!*

178. White scores neatly with *1* Kt×P! P×Kt; *2* Q×KP *ch,* K—R1; *3* Q—K7, Q—Kt1; *4* R×P *ch!* Q×R; *5* Q×R *ch,* Kt—B1; *6* Q×Kt *ch,* etc.

179. A famous Blackburne finish: *1* . . . Q—Kt8 *ch! 2* R×Q, Kt—B7 *ch; 3* K—Kt2, B—R6 *mate!*

180. Black wins at least a Pawn with *1* . . . Kt×QP! for instance *2* P×Kt, Kt—Q6 *ch; 3* K—Q2, Kt—B5; *4* Q—B3, Q—B7 *ch; 5* K—K1, Kt—Q6 *ch,* etc.

TENTH QUIZ

181

BLACK

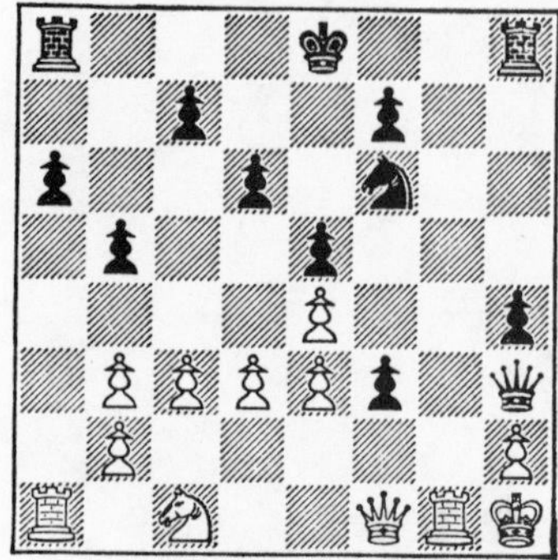

WHITE

Black moves

182

BLACK

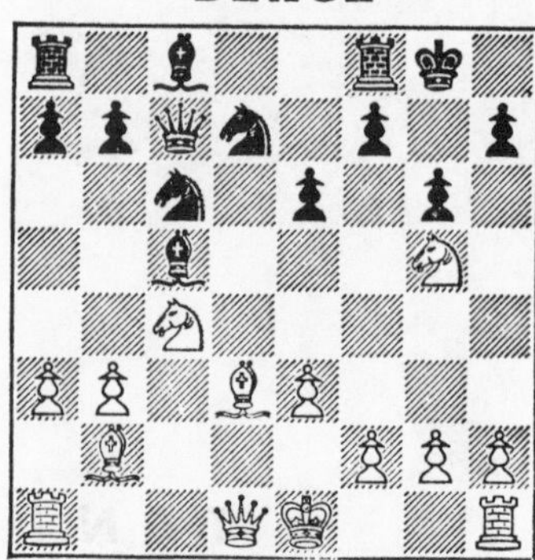

WHITE

White moves

183

BLACK

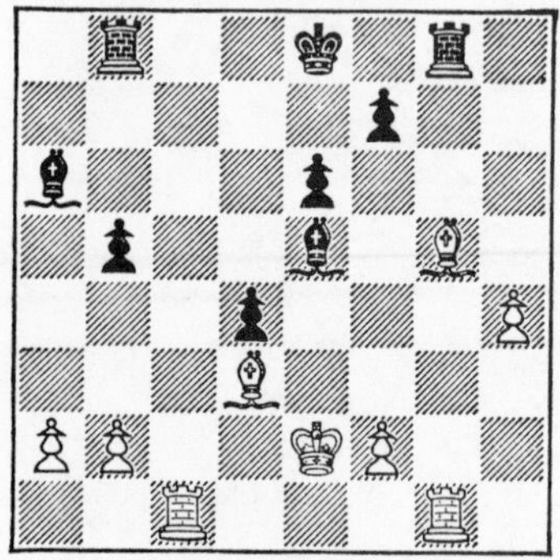

WHITE

White moves

184

BLACK

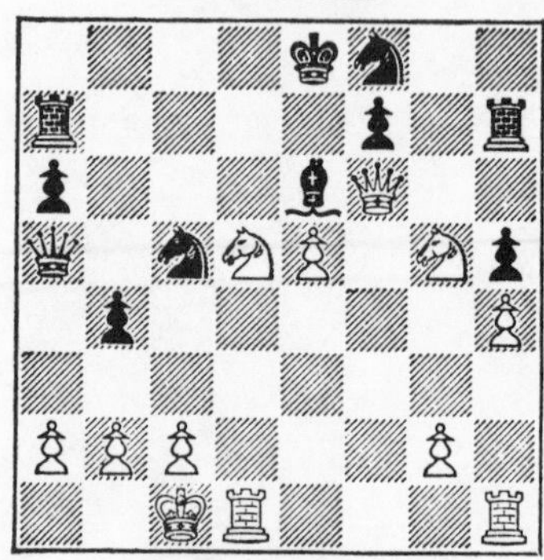

WHITE

White moves

181. Black wins prettily.
182. One brusque move forces Black's capitulation.
183. White clears the path for his KRP.
184. White's Queen plays an important role.

185

BLACK

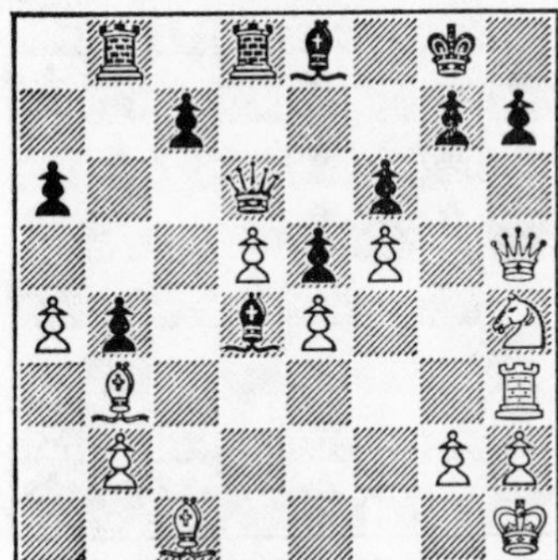

WHITE

White moves

186

BLACK

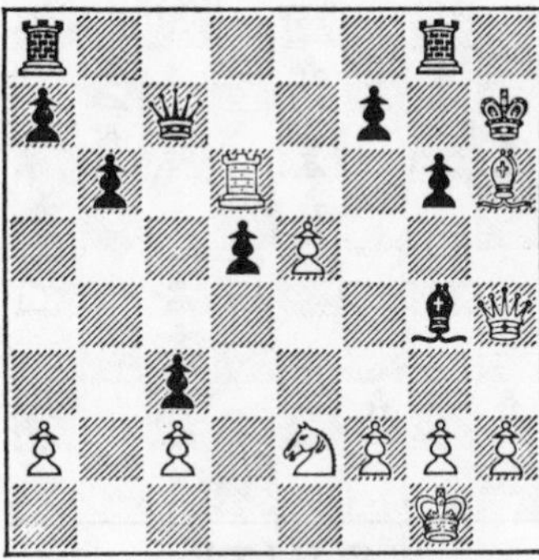

WHITE

White moves

187

BLACK

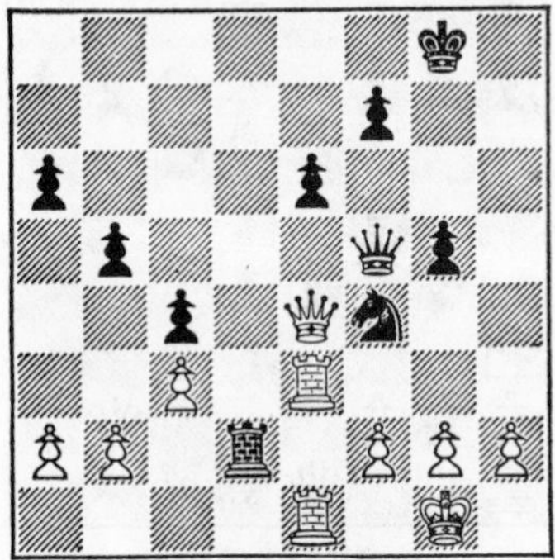

WHITE

Black moves

188

BLACK

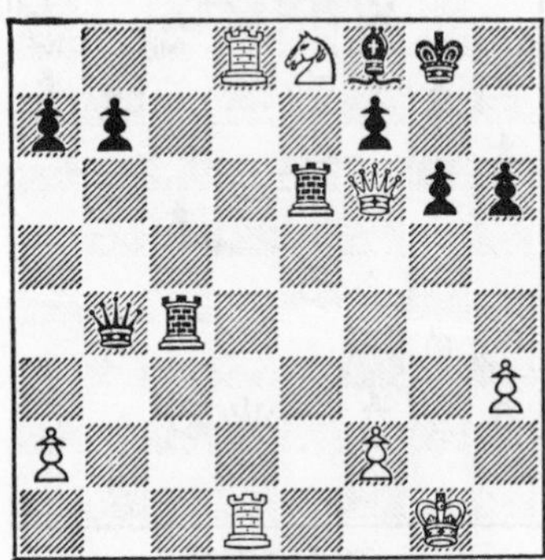

WHITE

White moves

185. White's concentration of force on the KR file achieves results.

186. White's Bishop has one right move.

187. Black wins neatly.

188. White's occupation of the last rank proves useful. The diversion comes just in time.

189

BLACK

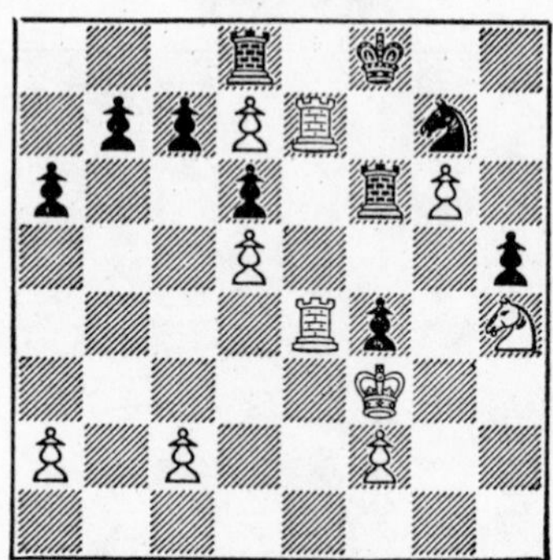

WHITE

White moves

190

BLACK

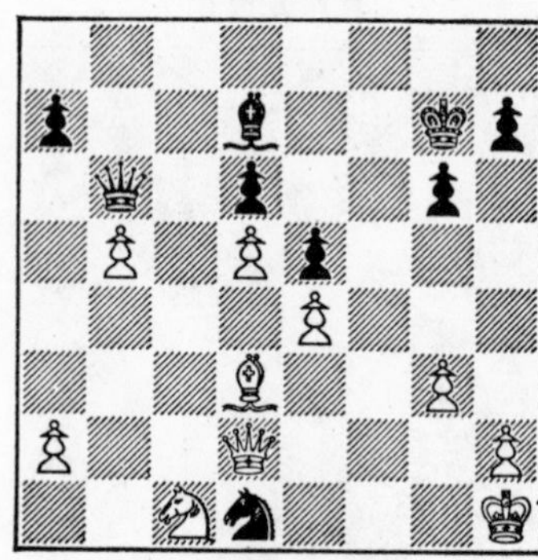

WHITE

Black moves

191

BLACK

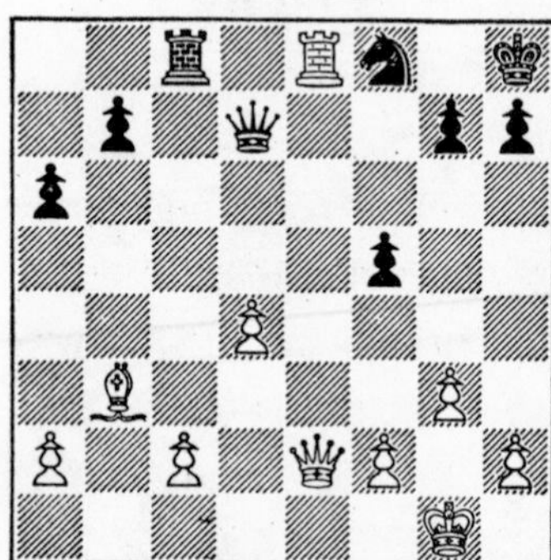

WHITE

White moves

192

BLACK

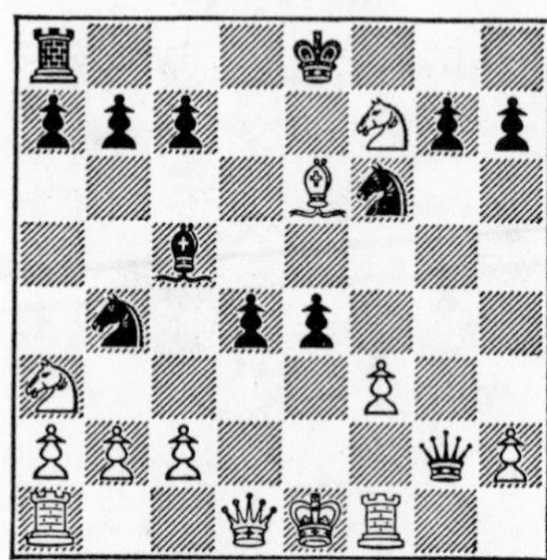

WHITE

Black moves

189. Illustrating finesses of Pawn promotion.

190. How does Black's Bishop participate in the attack?

191. White forces his opponent's resignation with . . . ?

192. Black sacrificed a Rook for this position.

193

BLACK

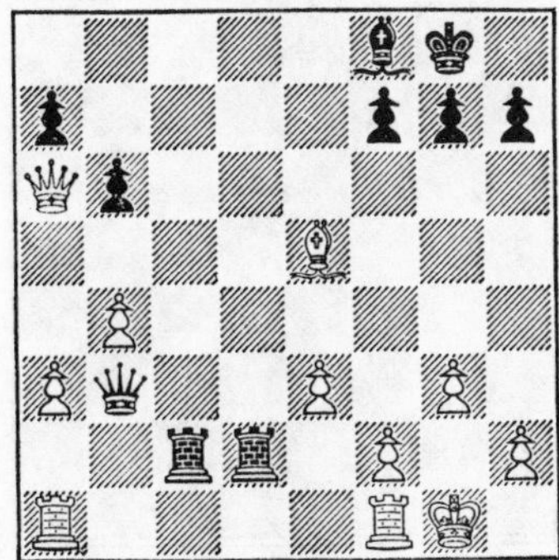

WHITE
Black moves

194

BLACK

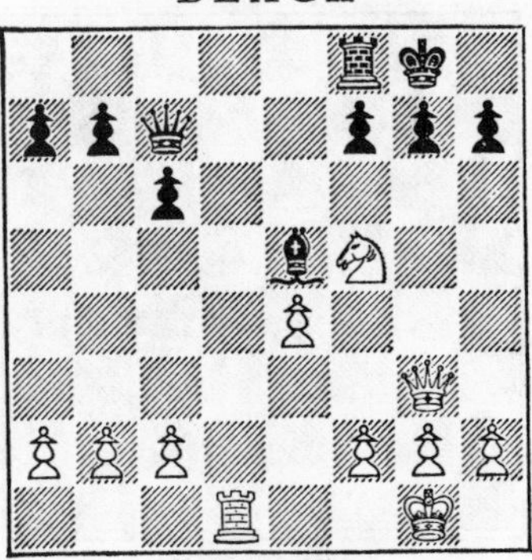

WHITE
White moves

195

BLACK

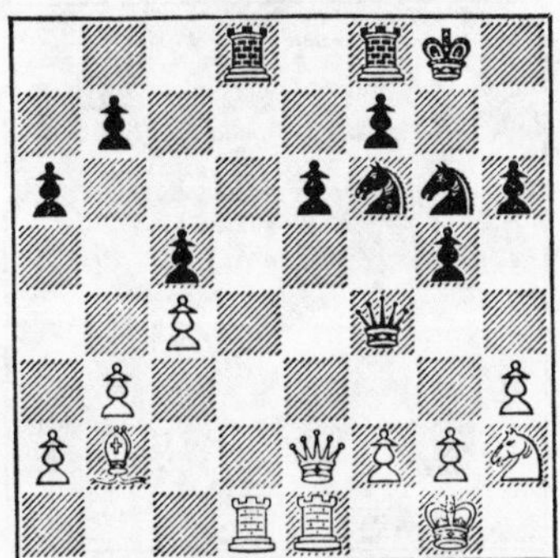

WHITE
White moves

196

BLACK

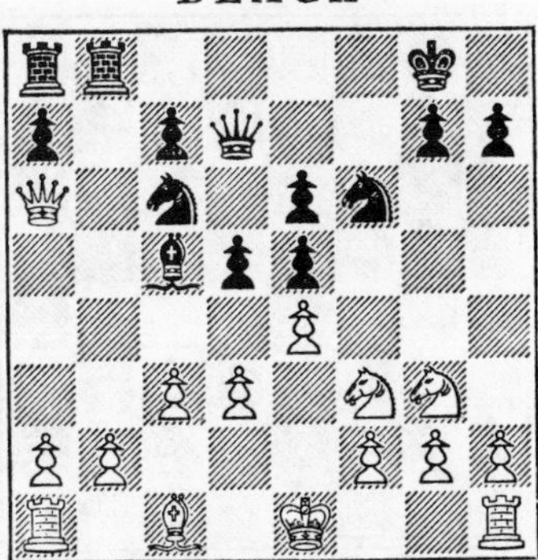

WHITE
Black moves

193. Capablanca demonstrates the power of the Rooks on the seventh rank.
194. A Capablanca win.
195. White wins a piece.
196. Tarrasch wins quickly. His clever combination is a sermon on the evils of Pawn-grabbing.

197

BLACK

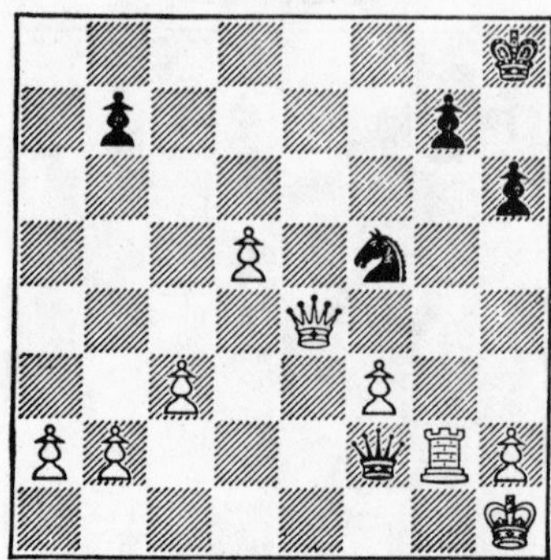

WHITE

Black moves

198

BLACK

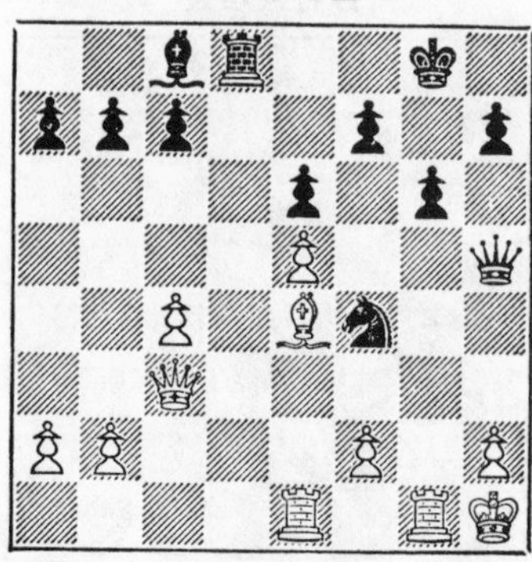

WHITE

Black moves

199

BLACK

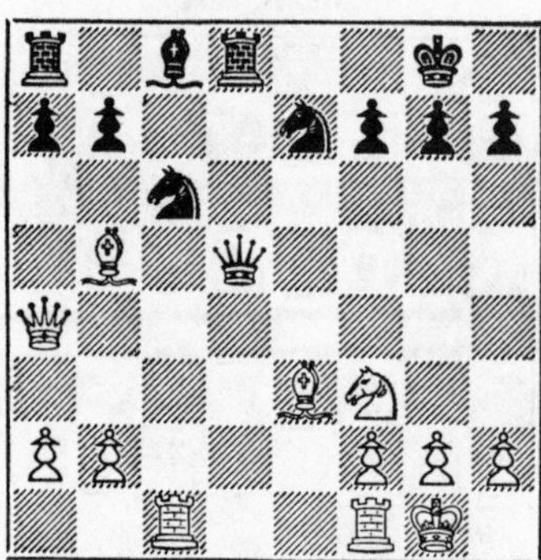

WHITE

White moves

200

BLACK

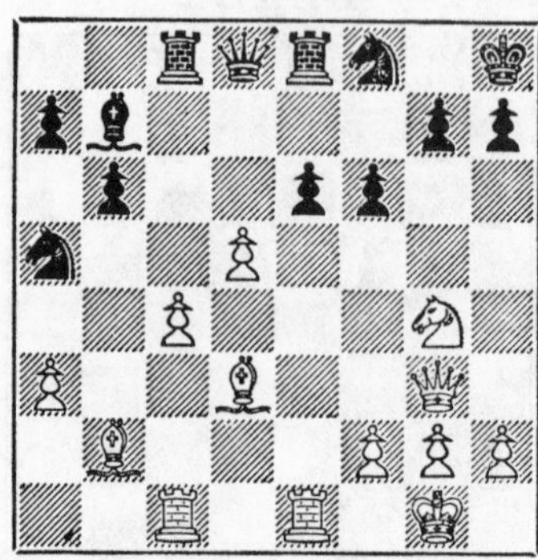

WHITE

White moves

197. White is in a mating net.
198. Black has a winning attack. In actual play, both masters failed to fathom the position.
199. Black's incomplete development spells trouble.
200. White's powerful attacking position decides.

TENTH QUIZ

181. There seems to be plenty of fight left in the position, but Black has an immediately decisive thrust: *1* . . . Kt—Kt5! White is helpless.

182. Black has erred in weakening the long diagonal and is drastically punished with *1* Q—R5! There is no defense.

183. White exploits the unprotected state of Black's KR and KB with *1* B—B6! R×R; *2* R×R, B—Q3; *3* R—Kt8 *ch,* B—B1; *4* P—R5 and Black is powerless against the further advance of the Pawn.

184. White has a problem mate with *1* Q—K7 *ch!* R×Q; *2* Kt—B6 *mate.*

185. The Queen sacrifice is obvious, but a fine point is needed to make it convincing: *1* Q×P *ch!* K×Q; *2* Kt—Kt6 *ch,* K—Kt1; *3* R—R8 *ch,* K—B2; *4* R—B8 *ch!* Q×R; *5* P—Q6 *mate.* Beware of masked discovered checks, as in # 168.

186. White has a pretty mate which was missed in actual play: *1* B—B8 *ch,* B—R4; *2* Q×B *ch!* P×Q; *3* R—R6 *mate!*

187. The curious move *1* . . . Kt—R6 *ch!* is decisive: *2* R×Kt (if 2 P×Kt, Q×P *ch* and mate follows), Q×Q and White cannot capture, as his first rank is not adequately protected.

188. A finish reminiscent of #184: *1* Q—Kt7 *ch!* B×Q; *2* Kt—B6 *mate.*

189. A good example of the power of passed Pawns: *1* R—K8 *ch!* Kt×R (if 1 . . . R×R; 2 R×R *ch,* Kt×R; 3 P—Q8(Q)); *2* R×Kt *ch!* R×R; *3* P—Kt7 *ch,* K—B2; *4* P×R(Q) *ch,* etc.

190. Black wins quickly with *1* . . . B—R6! *2* Q×Kt (what else?), Q—B7.

191. *1* Q–B4! and Black must resign.

192. A famous Morphy brilliancy: *1 . . .* Kt–Q6 *ch!* *2* Q×Kt (if 2 P×Kt, B–Kt5 *ch,* etc.), P×Q, etc.

193. The enormous power of the Rooks makes possible the decisive sacrifice *1 . . .* Q×KP! White cannot defend the BP, nor can he play *2* P×Q, R–Kt7 *ch; 3* K–R1, R×P *ch; 4* K–Kt1, R(B7)–Kt7 *mate.*

194. White (Capablanca) takes advantage of the inadequately protected first rank by playing *1* Kt–R6 *ch,* K–R1; *2* Q×B! Q×Q; *3* Kt×P *ch,* etc.

195. Black's Queen must guard the Knight at KB3. This is the basis for an unconventional attack: *1* P–Kt3! Q–B4; *2* Kt–Kt4!! and wins (if 2 . . . Kt×Kt; 3 P×Kt winning the Queen; if the attacked Knight retreats, then 3 Kt×P *ch* with the same result).

196. Black takes advantage of the awkward position of White's Queen by playing *1 . . .* Kt–QKt5! *2* P×Kt (2 Kt×P, Q–K1 is no better), B×KtP *ch; 3* B–Q2, R–Kt3. White's Queen is trapped!

197. Black wins surprisingly with *1 . . .* Q–B8 *ch!* *2* R–Kt1, Kt–Kt6 *ch! 3* P×Kt, Q–R6 *mate!*

198. Black could have won brilliantly with *1 . . .*R–Q6! *2* Q moves (if 2 B×R, Q–B6 *ch* and mate next move), Q×P *ch! 3* K×Q, R–R6 *mate!*

199. Again the inadequately protected first rank. Both players overlook that White wins with *1* KR–Q1, Q–R4 (if 1 . . . Q–K3; 2 B×Kt, Kt×B; 3 Q×Kt!); 2 B×Kt, Kt×B; *3* R×R *ch,* Kt×R; *4* Q–K8 *mate.* Another way is *1* B×Kt, Kt×B; *2* either R–Q1 leading to the same win.

200. White continues forcefully with *1* B×BP! for if *1 . . .* P×B; *2* Kt–R6 is deadly.

ELEVENTH QUIZ

201

BLACK

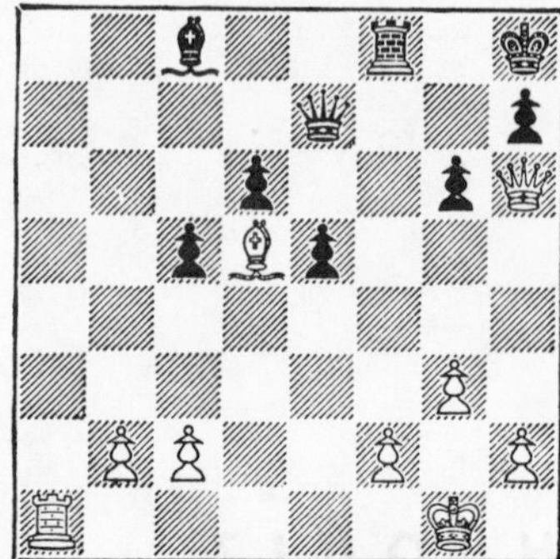

WHITE
White moves

202

BLACK

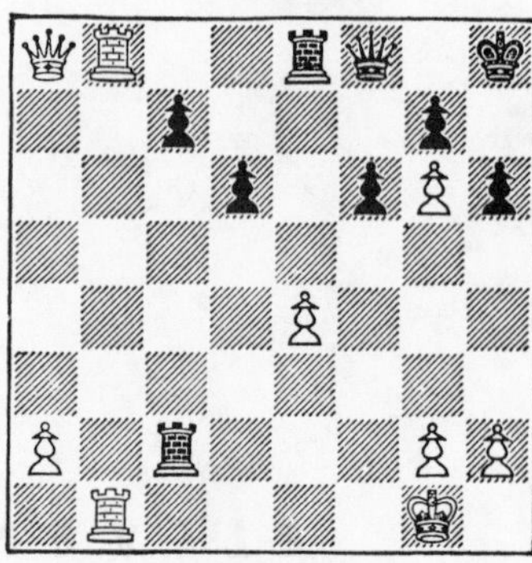

WHITE
Black moves

203

BLACK

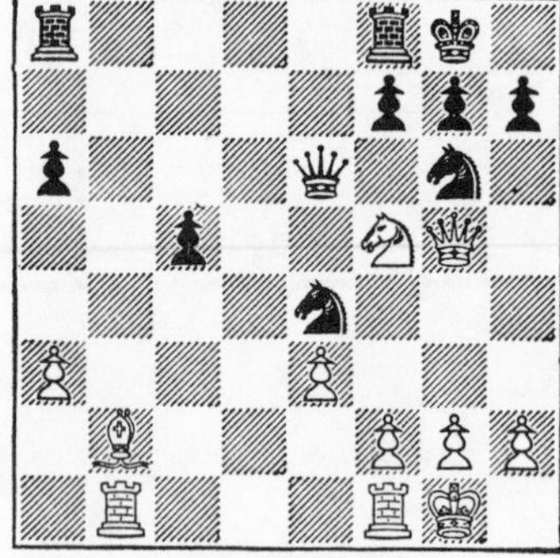

WHITE
White moves

204

BLACK

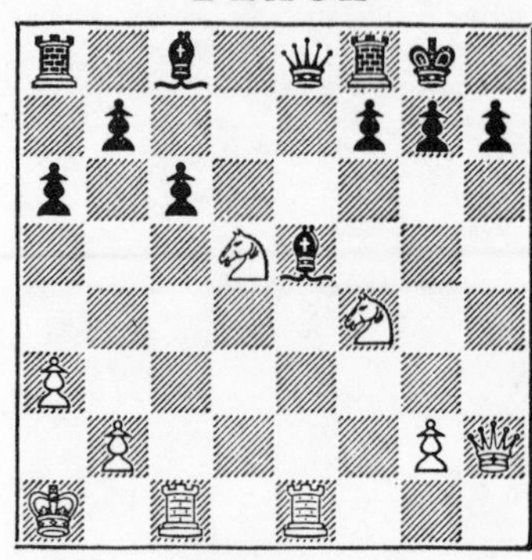

WHITE
White moves

201. Black's Queen has too many burdens.
202. Black resigned in this position!
203. White decides the game at once.
204. White has a beautiful win.

205

BLACK

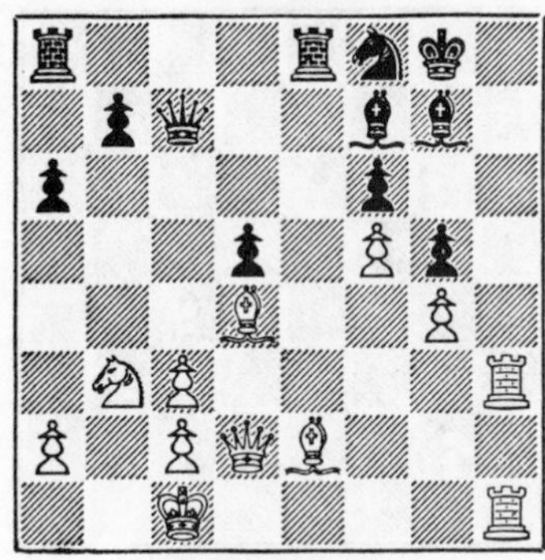

WHITE
White moves

206

BLACK

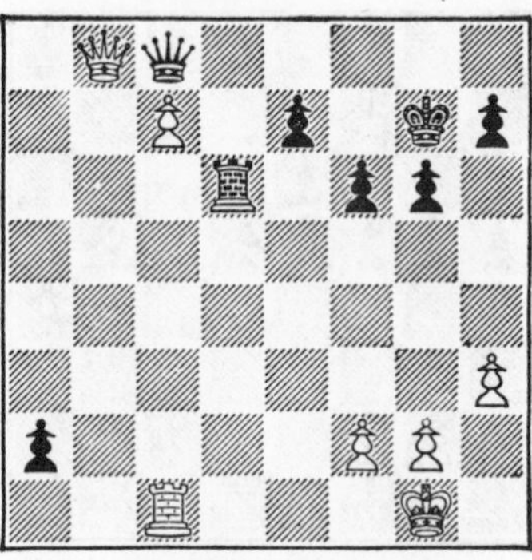

WHITE
Black moves

207

BLACK

WHITE
White moves

208

BLACK

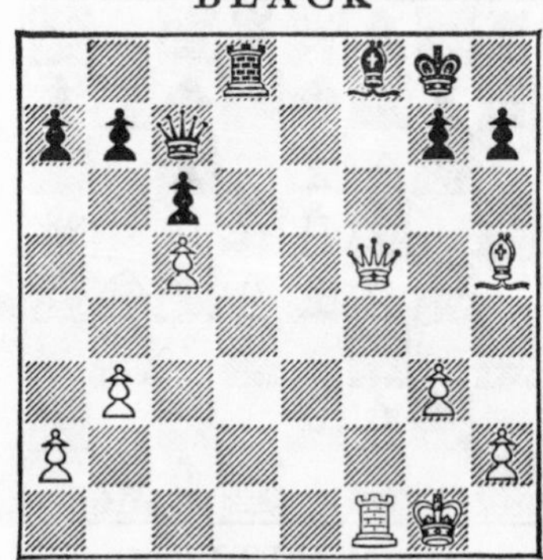

WHITE
White moves

205. What is the most forceful method for White?

206. Can Black save himself?

207. The game is still in the opening, and yet. . . .

208. A subtle maneuver decides.

209

BLACK

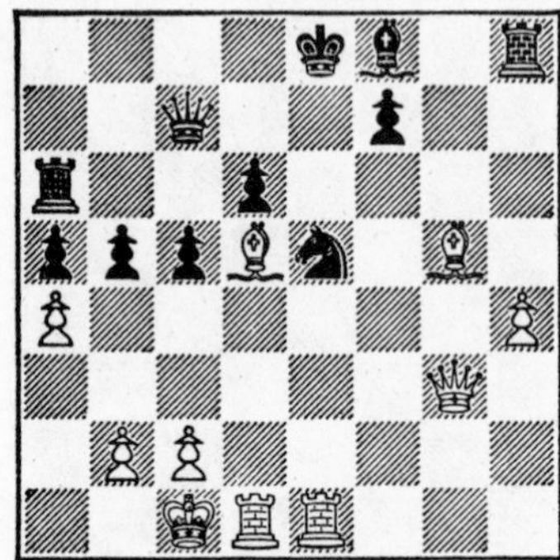

WHITE

White moves

210

BLACK

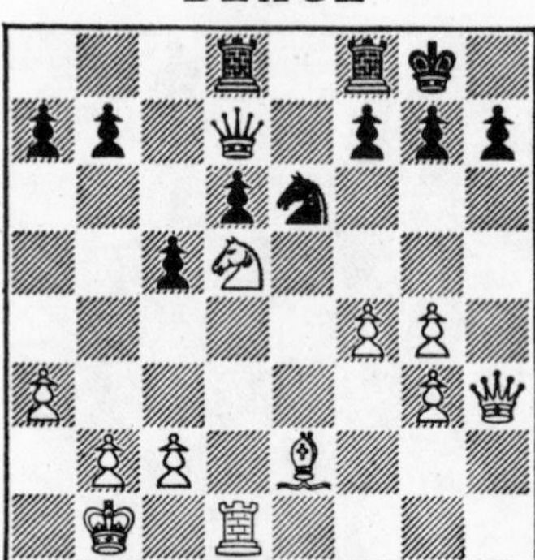

WHITE

White moves

211

BLACK

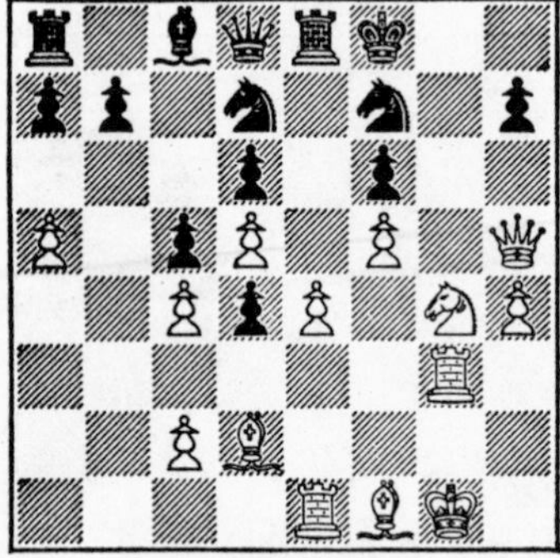

WHITE

White moves

212

BLACK

WHITE

White moves

209. Black's King is precariously situated in the center.
210. Black's Queen must be driven away.
211. Black's game is hopelessly cramped.
212. Black's King is helpless. But how does White start the ball rolling?!

213

BLACK

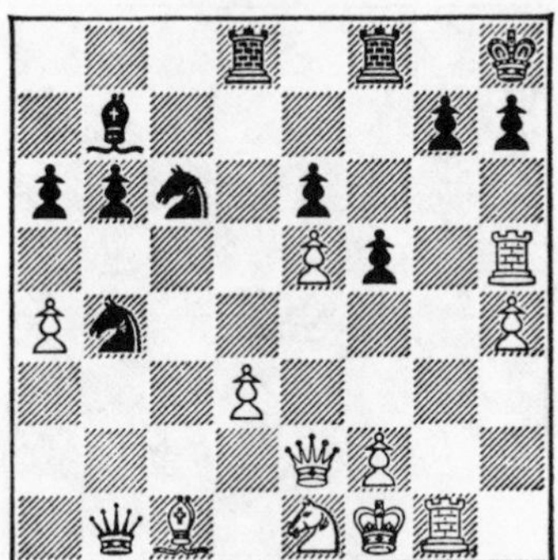

WHITE
White moves

214

BLACK

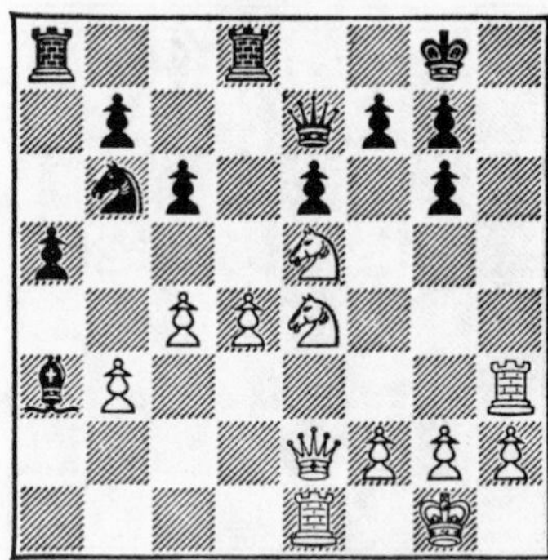

WHITE
White moves

215

BLACK

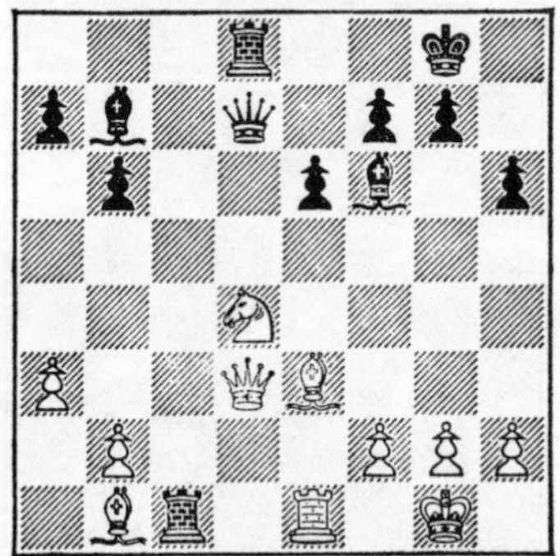

WHITE
White moves

216

BLACK

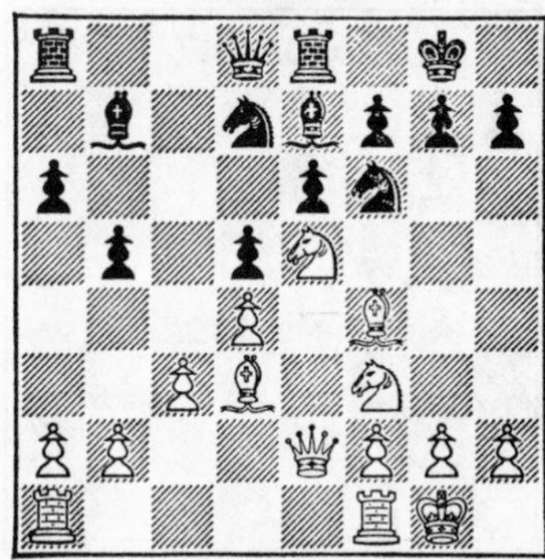

WHITE
White moves

213. White's attack hits home first.

214. White's Knights perform superbly.

215. White looks for the best move.

216. Black's position is less solid than it looks.

217

BLACK

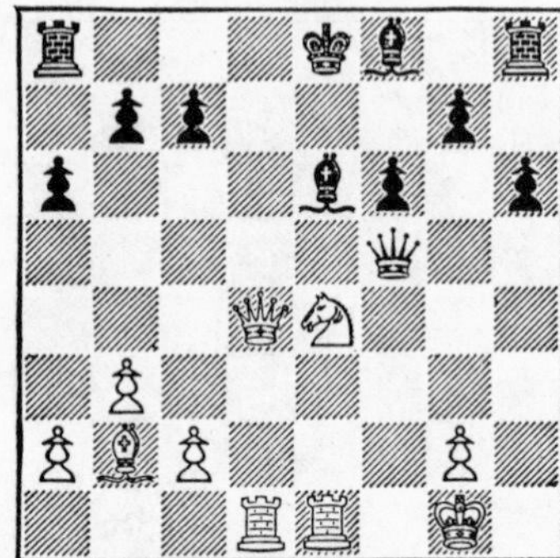

WHITE
White moves

218

BLACK

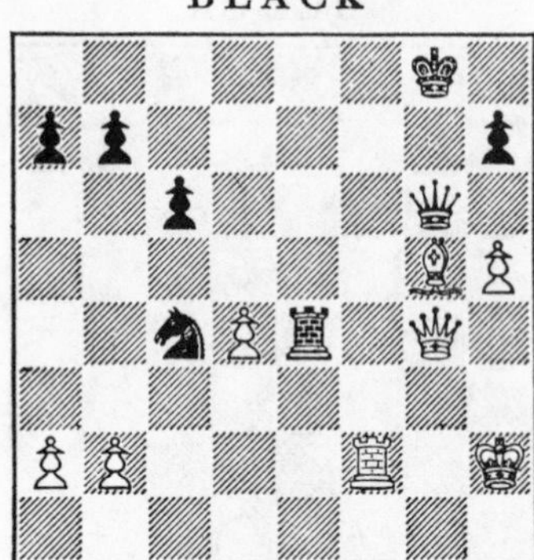

WHITE
White moves

219

BLACK

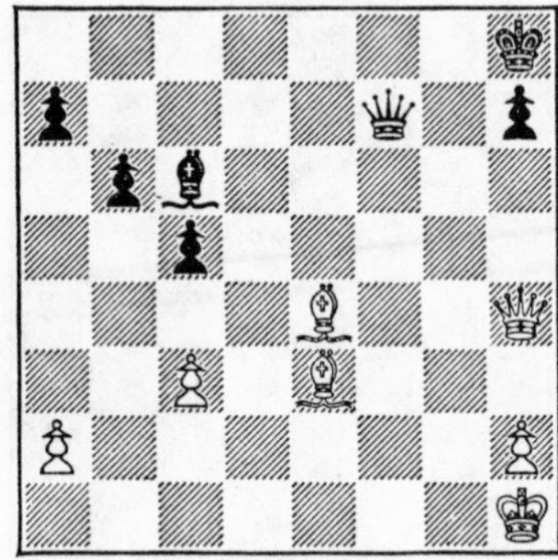

WHITE
Black moves

220

BLACK

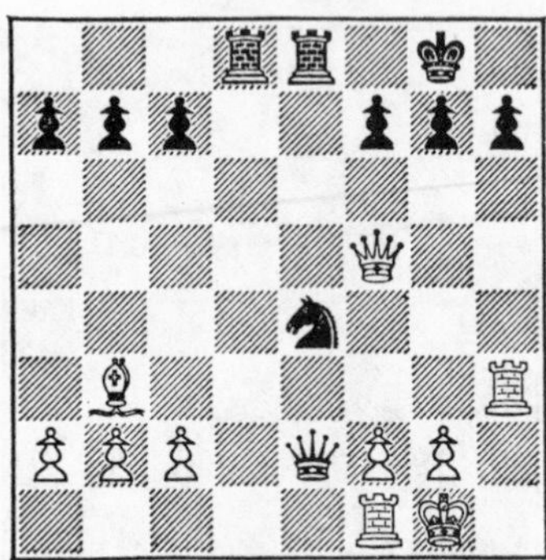

WHITE
Black moves

217. Black's King is on the open K file.

218. One of Marshall's prettiest combinations.

219. A Pillsbury blindfold gem.

220. White's attacking formation is deceptive.

ELEVENTH QUIZ

201. One addition to the attacking forces decides the game immediately: *1* R—R7! and Black has no satisfactory reply.

202. Black is in a terrible predicament, from which he could have extricated himself with *1* . . . R×RP!! Instead, he resigned.

203. Black's position seems most promising, but he has overlooked a deadly stroke: *1* Q—R6! forcing mate!

204. A curious position, in which White forces the win with *1* R×B! Q×R; *2* Kt—KKt6! The observant reader will have recognized this position as a more elaborate setting of #77.

205. White's splendid attacking position gives him the opportunity for *1* Q×P! B—Kt3 (. . . P×Q allows mate in two); *2* P×B!

206. Black is apparently lost, but he finds a clever resource to save the game: *1* . . . R—B3!! (if 2 R×R? P—R8(Q) *ch;* 2 K—R2, Q—K4 *ch* followed by . . . Q×Q).

207. In this seemingly innocent position, White has a forced win with *1* Q×P *ch!!* K×Q; *2* R—Kt3 *ch,* K—R3; *3* B—B1 *ch,* etc.

208. White wins elegantly with *1* B—B7 *ch,* K—R1; *2* B—K8!!

209. It is clear that something drastic is likely to happen to Black's King, but the finish is artistic: *1* R×Kt *ch,* P×R; *2* Q×P *ch!* Q×Q; *3* B—B6 *ch,* R×B; *4* R—Q8 *mate.*

210. A most unusual conclusion: *1* B—Kt5!! wins the Queen, for if *1* . . . Q×B; *2* Kt—K7 *ch,* K—R1; *3* Q×P *ch!* K×R; *4* R—R1 *mate.*

211. Black is tied up in knots, and the end comes

quickly: *1* Q×Kt *ch!* K×Q; *2* Kt—R6 *ch,* K—B1; *3* R—Kt8 *ch,* K—K2; *4* R—Kt7 *ch,* K—B1; *5* R—B7 *mate.*

212. The exposed position of Black's King allows his opponent to take liberties: *1* Q×P *ch!* B×Q; *2* R—B7 *ch,* K—Q3; *3* Kt—Kt5 *ch,* K—Q4; *4* P—B4 *ch,* K—K5; *5* R—K1 *mate.*

213. Black's pieces are poorly posted for defense purposes, making the following remarkable finish possible: *1* R×P *ch!* K×R; *2* Q—R5 *ch,* K—Kt1; *3* R×P *ch!* K×R; *4* B—R6 *ch,* K—R2; *5* B—Kt5 *ch!* K—Kt2; *6* Q—R6 *ch,* K—Kt1; *7* Q—Kt6 *ch,* K—R1; *8* B—B6 *ch,* R×B; *9* P×R, R—Q2; *10* Q—K8 *ch,* K—R2; *11* Q×R *ch* followed by mate.

214. White (Yates) wins by *1* Kt—Kt5!! Black resigned because of the following possibilities: *1* . . . Q×Kt; *2* R—R8 *ch!* or *1* . . . R—KB1; *2* Kt(Kt5)×BP! R×Kt; *3* Kt×KtP leaving Black defenseless.

215. Black is overtaken by a catastrophe: *1* Q—R7 *ch,* K—B1; *2* Q—R8 *ch,* K—K2; *3* Kt—B5 *ch!* P×Kt; *4* B—B5 *mate!*

216. White wins a Pawn with *1* Kt×P! for if *1* . . . K×Kt; *2* Q×P *ch!!* K×R (or 2 . . . K—B1; 3 Kt—Kt5); *3* Kt—Kt5 *mate!* An echo of a famous combination.

217. *1* Q—Q7 *ch!!* B×Q; *2* Kt—Q6 *ch,* K—Q1; *3* Kt—B7 *ch,* K—B1; *4* R—K8 *ch!* B×R; *5* R—Q8 *mate.*

218. White (Marshall) decides the game with a really exquisite move: *1* B—R6!! and Black resigns!

219. One of Pillsbury's blindfold brilliancies: *1* . . . Q—B8 *ch!* *2* B—Kt1, Q—B6 *ch!!* *3* B×Q, B×B *mate.* An extraordinary position.

220. Black wins by clever use of his Knight: *1* . . . Q×R *ch!* *2* K×Q, Kt—Q7 *ch;* *3* K—Kt1, R—K8 *ch;* *4* K—R2, Kt—B8 *ch;* *5* K—Kt1, Kt—Kt6 *ch* (or . . . Kt—K6 *ch*); *6* K—R2, Kt×Q with a Rook to the good.

TWELFTH QUIZ

221

BLACK

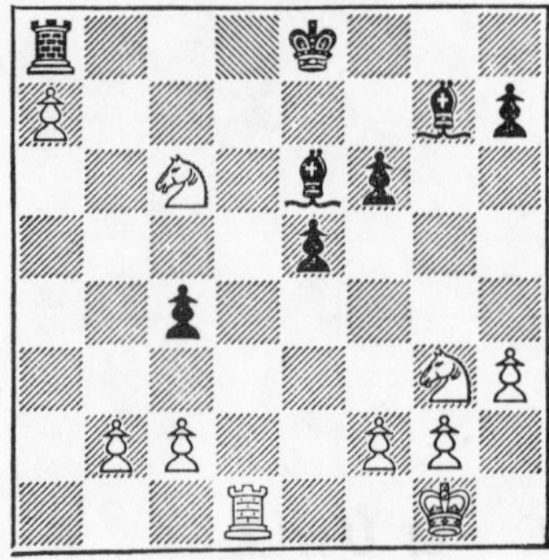

WHITE

White moves

222

BLACK

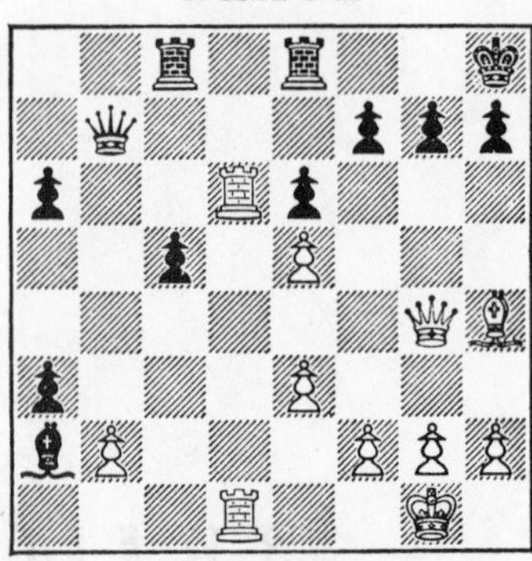

WHITE

White moves

223

BLACK

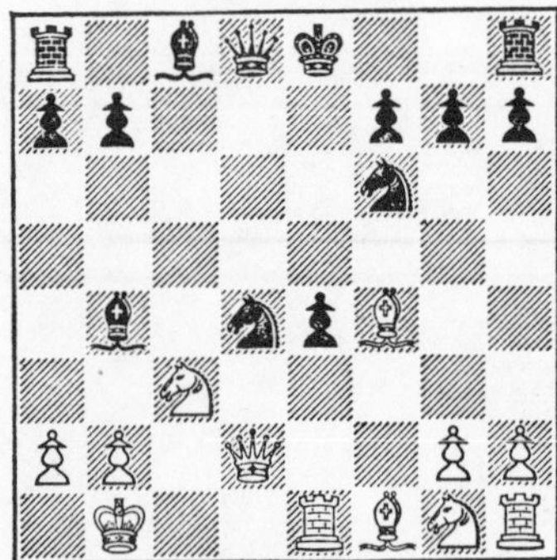

WHITE

White moves

224

BLACK

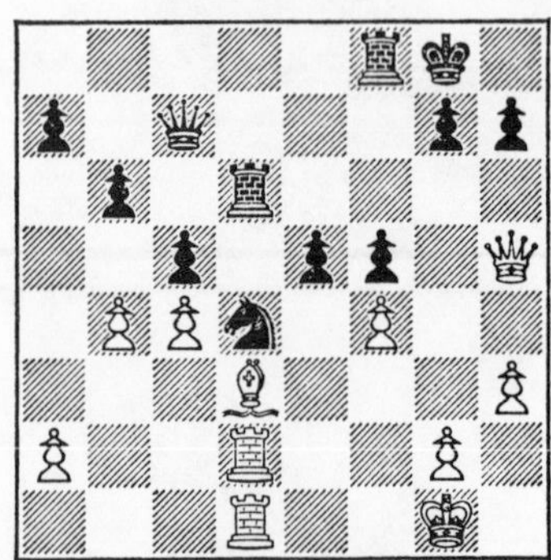

WHITE

Black moves

221. Yates missed a pretty win here.
222. Black is in a mating net. White's play is ingenious.
223. Again the Black King is on the K file.
224. White's Queen is in danger.

225

BLACK

WHITE

Black moves

226

BLACK

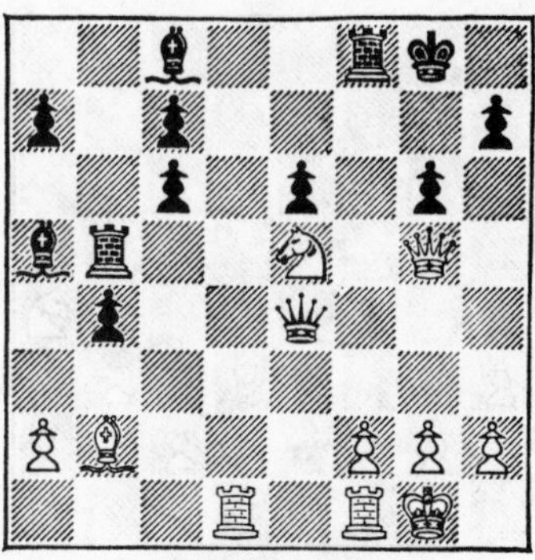

WHITE

White moves

227

BLACK

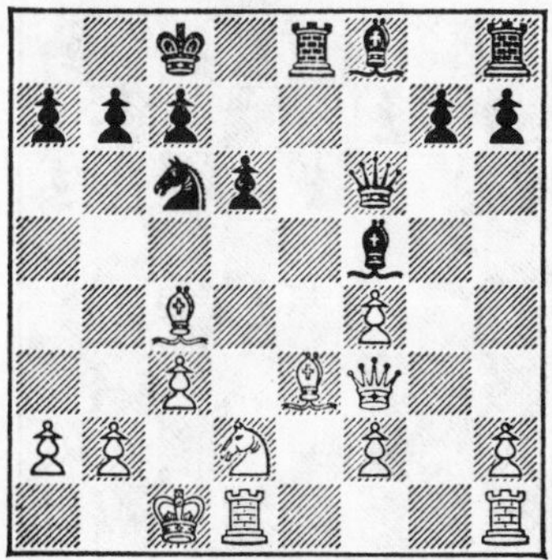

WHITE

Black moves

228

BLACK

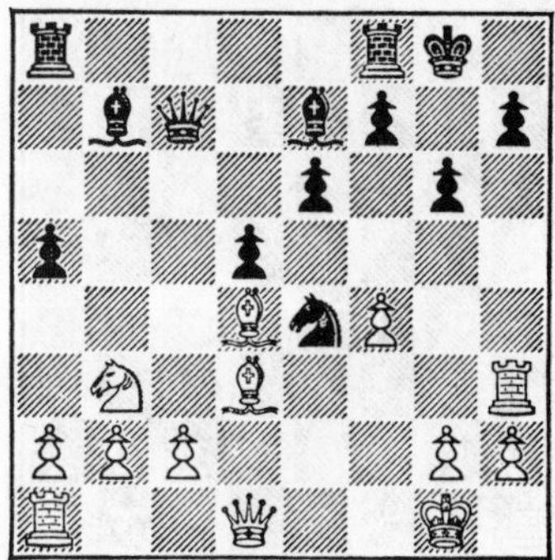

WHITE

White moves

225. The Bishops assert themselves.
226. The long diagonal plays its proverbial role.
227. Black wins a piece.
228. White wins a piece. The hostile King is not adequately guarded.

229

BLACK

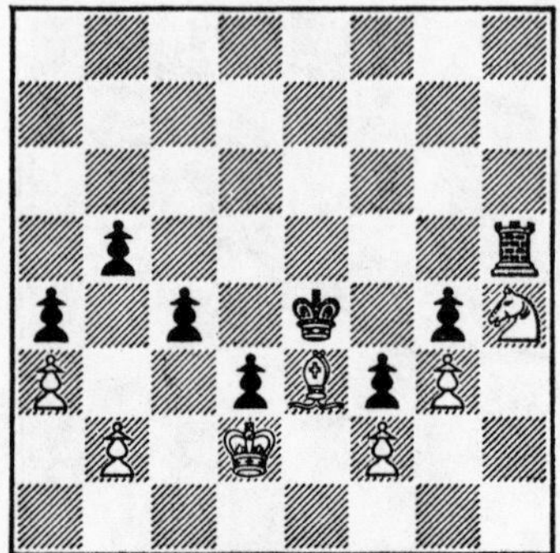

WHITE

Black moves

230

BLACK

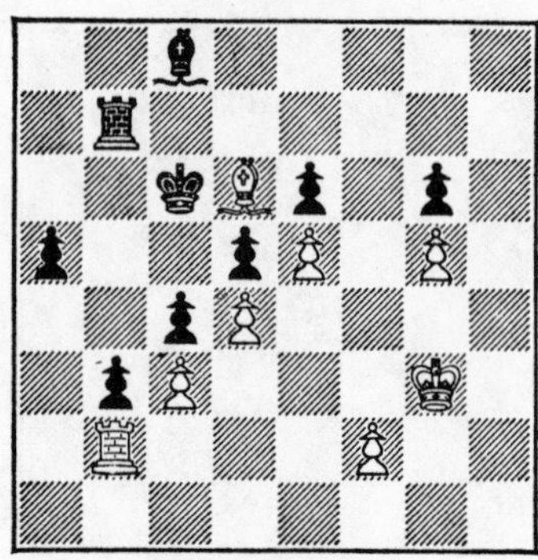

WHITE

Black moves

231

BLACK

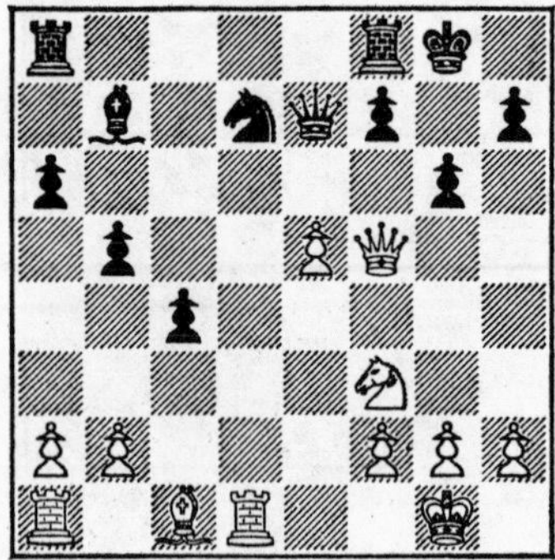

WHITE

White moves

232

BLACK

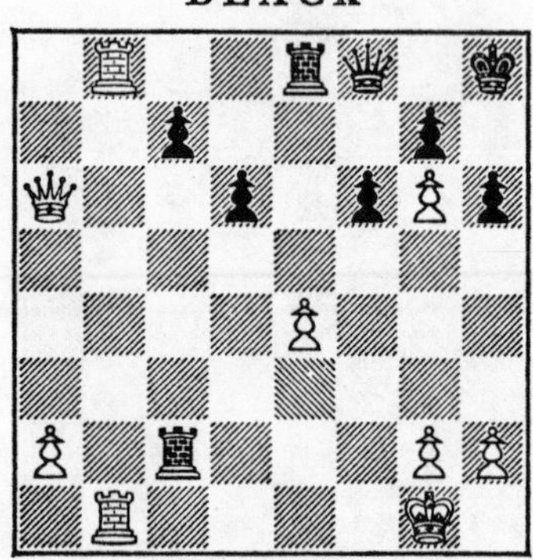

WHITE

White moves

229. How does Nimzovich break through?
230. Another brilliant Nimzovich breakthrough.
231. What is White's strongest move?
232. Capablanca blundered in this position.

233

BLACK

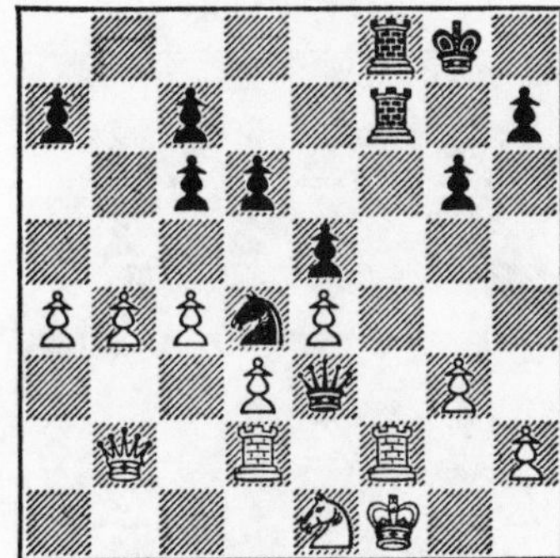

WHITE

Black moves

234

BLACK

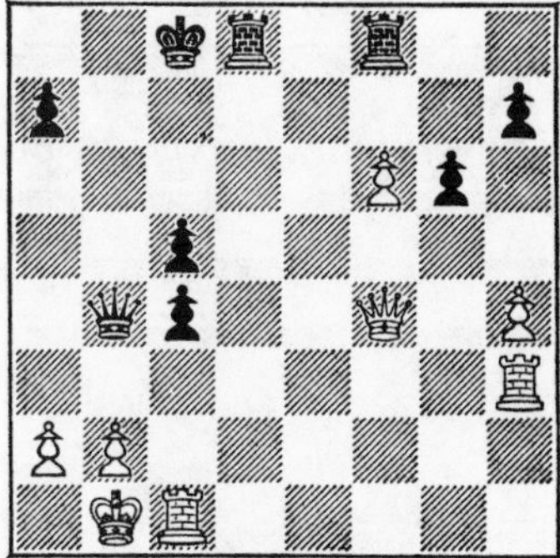

WHITE

White moves

235

BLACK

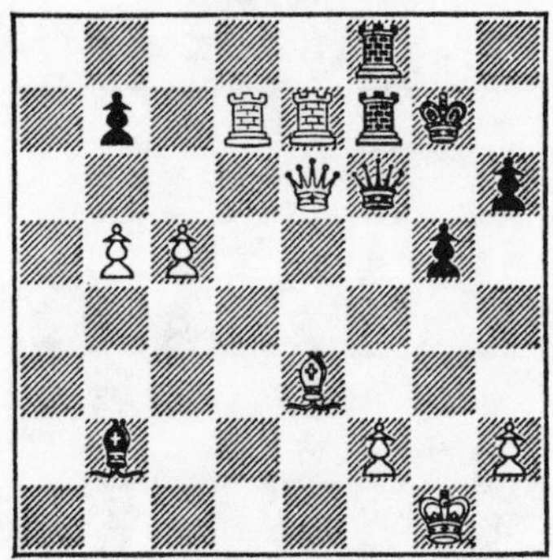

WHITE

White moves

236

BLACK

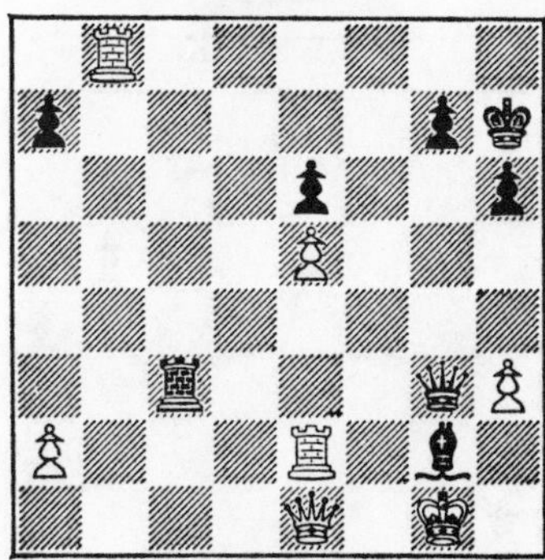

WHITE

Black moves

233. A brillancy prize win by Gunsberg.

234. White relies on the pinning motif.

235. A far-sighted combination by White.

236. Black simplifies neatly. (Missed in actual play.)

237

BLACK

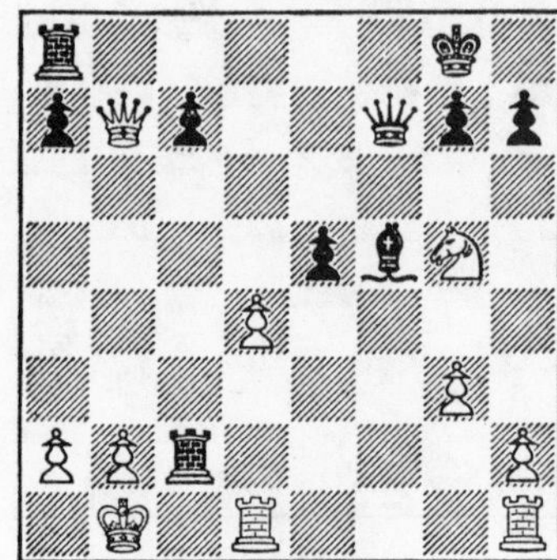

WHITE

Black moves

238

BLACK

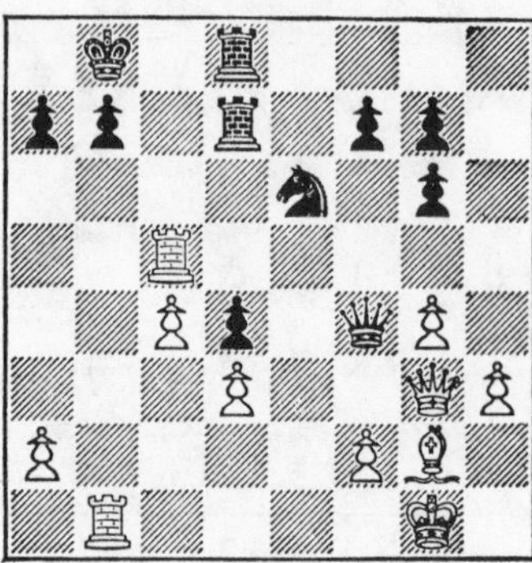

WHITE

White moves

239

BLACK

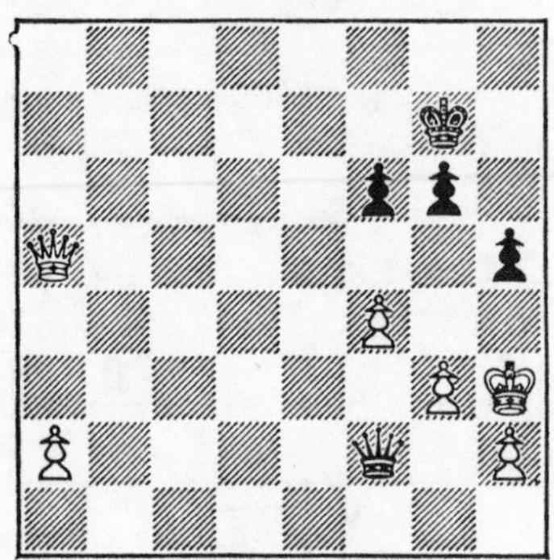

WHITE

Black moves

240

BLACK

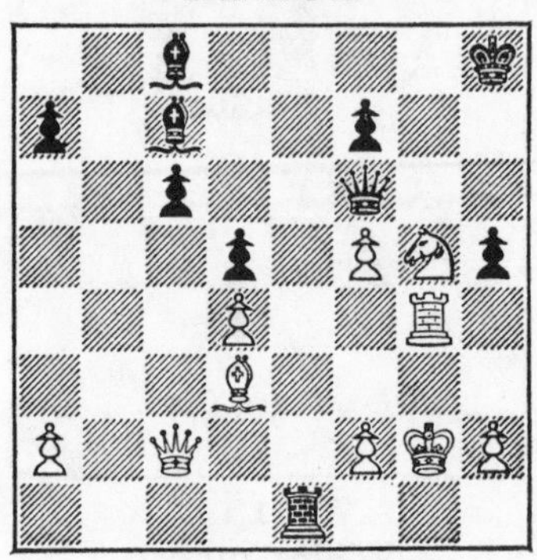

WHITE

White moves

237. What is the strongest discovered check?
238. How is White to continue the attack?
239. An ingenious Marshall win.
240. Spielmann forces his opponent's resignation.

TWELFTH QUIZ

221. White wins a piece by a delightful combination: *1* R—Q8 *ch!* R×R; *2* Kt×R, B—Q4; *3* Kt—K6!! and one of the Bishops must go, as Black cannot guard against the double threat of Kt—B7 *ch* and Kt×B *ch.*

222. Black's pieces are posted very poorly for defensive purposes, so that White forces the game with *1* B—B6! P×B (or 1 . . . KR—Kt1; 2 Q×P *ch!* R×Q; 3 R—Q8 *ch,* etc.); *2* P×P, KR—Kt1; *3* R—Q8! and Black is helpless.

223. Black has overextended himself and he has committed a cardinal mistake in not castling. White wins a piece with *1* Kt×P! leaving Black without a wholly satisfactory reply. If *1* . . . B×Q; *2* Kt×Kt *ch,* K—B1; *3* B—Q6 *ch,* Q×B; *4* R—K8 *mate.*

224. White's Queen has wandered too far afield. Black plays *1* . . . R—R3; *2* Q—Kt5, Kt—B6 *ch!* *3* P×Kt, R—Kt3 winning the Queen.

225. Black winds up the game explosively with a problem-like finish: *1* . . . Q—R5 *ch!!* *2* K×Q, B—B7 *ch;* *3* K—Kt5, P—R3 *mate!*

226. The long diagonal proves its worth with *1* Kt—B7!! (not 1 Kt—Kt4? Q×P *ch!*), R×Kt; *2* R—Q8 *ch,* R—B1; *3* Q—B6.

227. Black wins a piece in astonishing fashion with *1* . . . P—Q4!! White's KB must sit tight, for if *2* B×P (or 2 Q×P), Q×P *ch!!* *3* P×Q, B—R6 *mate.*

228. Once more the strength of the long diagonal is demonstrated, for *1* B×Kt wins a piece: *1* . . . P×B; *2* Q—R5!!

229. A characteristically profound Nimzovich finish: *1* . . . P—Kt5! *2* P×P, R×Kt! *3* P×R, P—Kt6; *4* P×P, P—B6 *ch!* *5* P×P, P—R6 and wins.

230. Another Nimzovich combination: *1* . . . R–Kt5!! *2* P×R (or 2 B×R, P×B; 3 P×P, K–Kt4, etc.), P–R5; *3* P–Kt5 *ch,* K×P; *4* B–R3, P–B6; *5* R–Kt1, K–B5 and wins.

231. A tricky position. White wins at least the exchange with *1* B–Kt5! (but not 1 Q×Kt? or 1 R×Kt? when Black wins by playing a Rook to Q1).

232. *1* R×R! Q×R; *2* Q–R4! wins.

233. Black has an overwhelmingly superior position and forces the game with *1* . . . Kt–Kt6! (the main variation is 2 R–K2, R×R *ch;* 3 R×R, Kt–Q7 *ch*).

234. White exploits the exposed position of the hostile King with the pretty move *1* R–QKt3!

235. White wins by means of a subtle combination: *1* Q×R *ch!* (or 1 R×R *ch* leading to the same position), R×Q; *2* R×R *ch,* Q×R; *3* P–B6! (the point) P×P; *4* P×P, B–K4 (if 4 . . . Q×R; 5 P×Q, B–B3; 6 B–Q4); *5* B–Q4! B×B; *6* R×Q *ch,* K×R; *7* P–B7 and wins. White's double use of the pin creates a really exquisite effect.

236. Black has a clever win: *1* . . . R–B8! *2* Q×R, B–B6 *ch;* *3* K–B1, B×R *ch;* *4* K×B, Q×P *ch* and wins.

237. An exciting position: *1* . . . R–B8 *ch!* *2* K×R, Q–B5 *ch;* *3* K–Q2, Q–Q6 *ch;* *4* K–K1, Q–K6 *ch;* *5* K–B1, R–KB1 and wins.

238. Black seems to be adequately protected, but White wins with *1* B×P! R×B; *2* R×R *ch,* K×R; *3* Q–Kt2 *ch* and mate is unavoidable.

239. Black (Marshall) wins by force: *1* . . . Q–B8 *ch;* *2* K–R4, Q–Kt7; *3* P–KR3, Q–K5! *4* Q–R3, P–Kt4 *ch;* *5* K×P,Q–K7 *ch!* *6* P–Kt4, Q–K1 *mate.*

240. White (Spielmann) wins beautifully with *1* Q×P!! Q×Q; *2* Kt×P *ch,* K–R2; *3* P–B6 *ch,* R–K5; *4* R–Kt7 *mate.*

THIRTEENTH QUIZ

241

BLACK

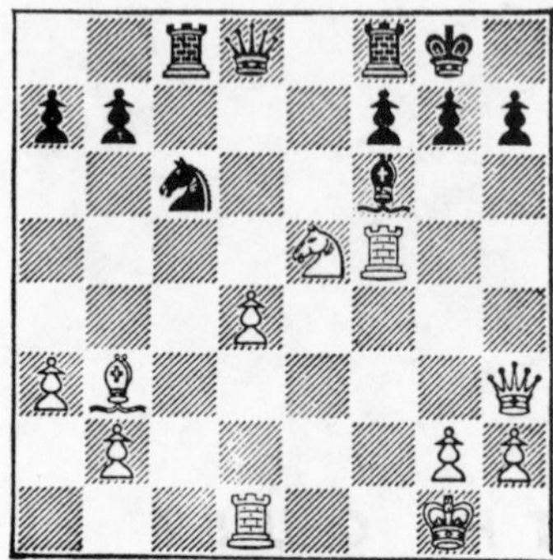

WHITE

White moves

242

BLACK

WHITE

White moves

243

BLACK

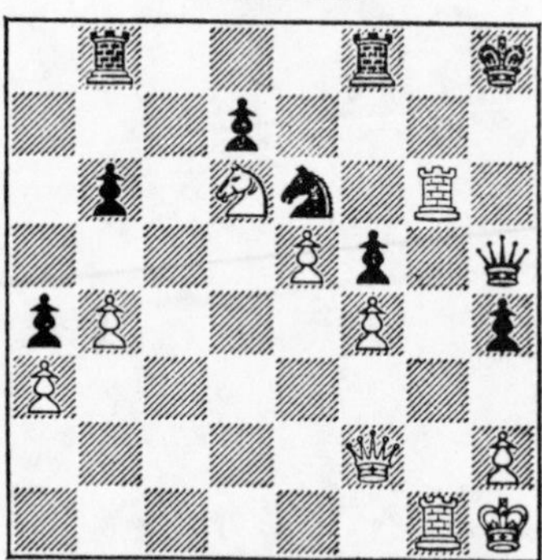

WHITE

White moves

244

BLACK

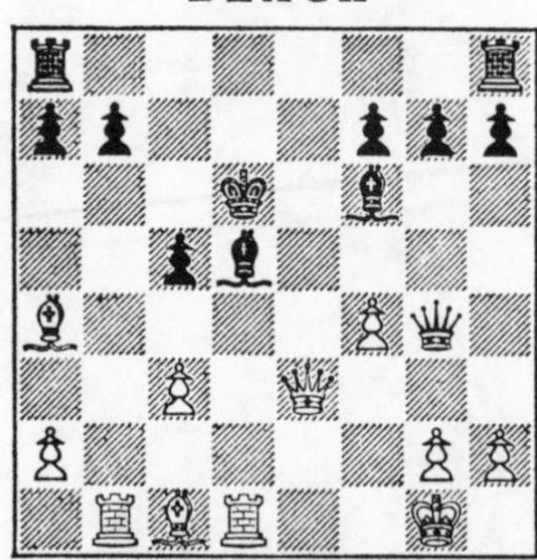

WHITE

White moves

241. An unexpected combination wins quickly for White.

242. Rubinstein utilizes the long diagonal.

243. Black is helpless against the Rooks.

244. Black's King suffers the usual fate of an exposed monarch.

245

BLACK

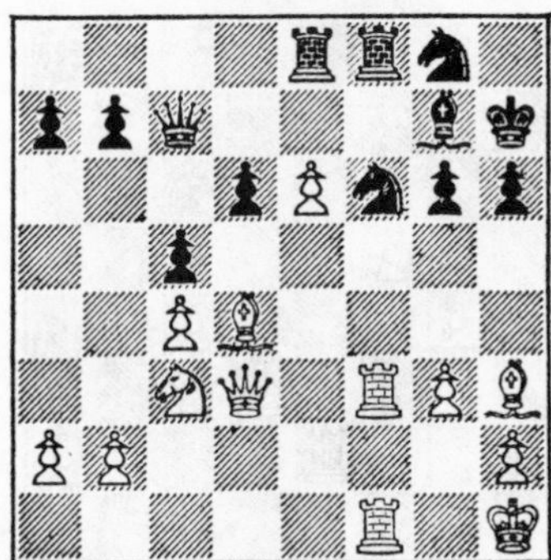

WHITE

White moves

246

BLACK

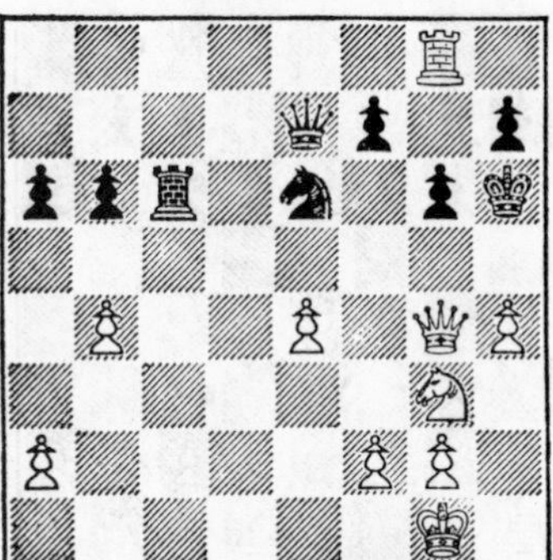

WHITE

White moves

247

BLACK

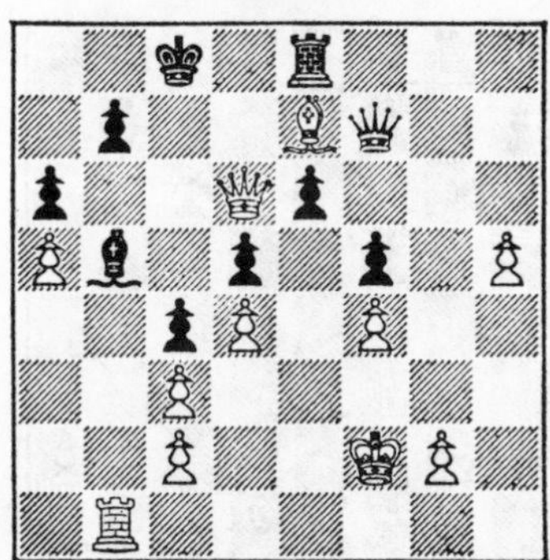

WHITE

White moves

248

BLACK

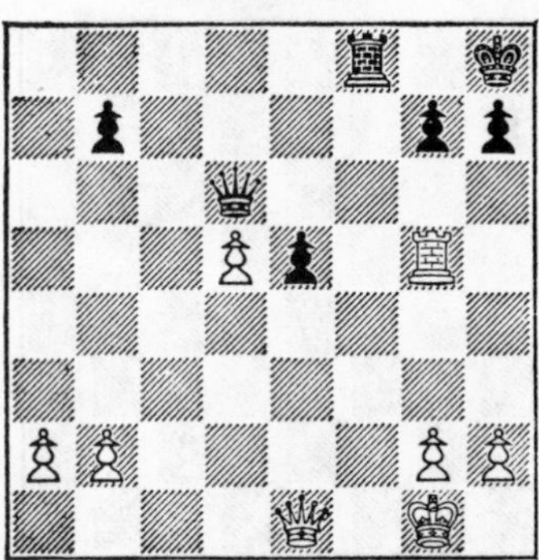

WHITE

Black moves

245. And here the Black King is much less secure than one would think.
246. White finds a charming conclusion which is most artistic.
247. A magnificent finish from an R. A. F. Tournament.
248. Black exploits White's helplessness on the first rank.

249

BLACK

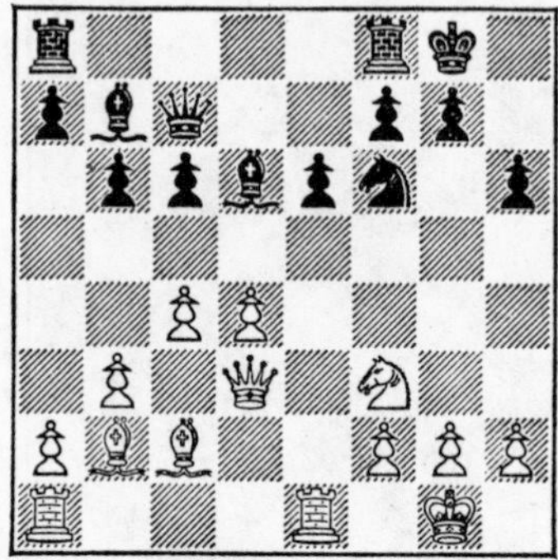

WHITE

White moves

250

BLACK

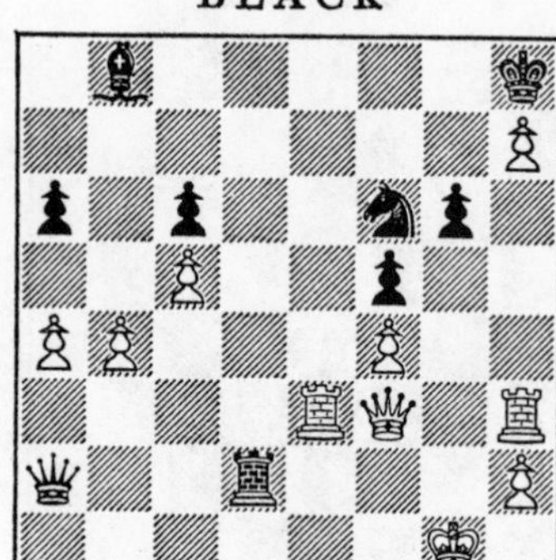

WHITE

White moves

251

BLACK

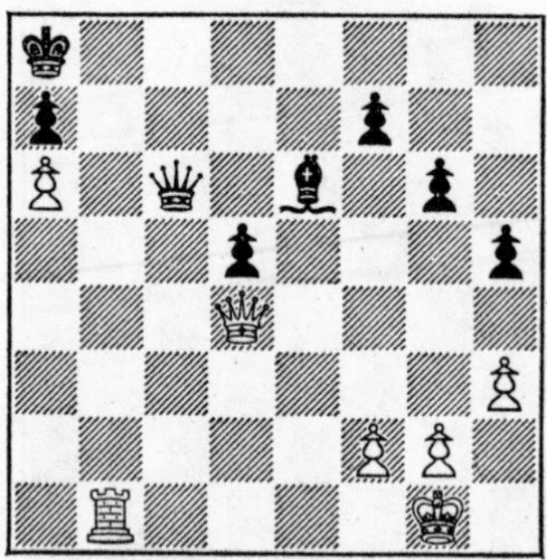

WHITE

White moves

252

BLACK

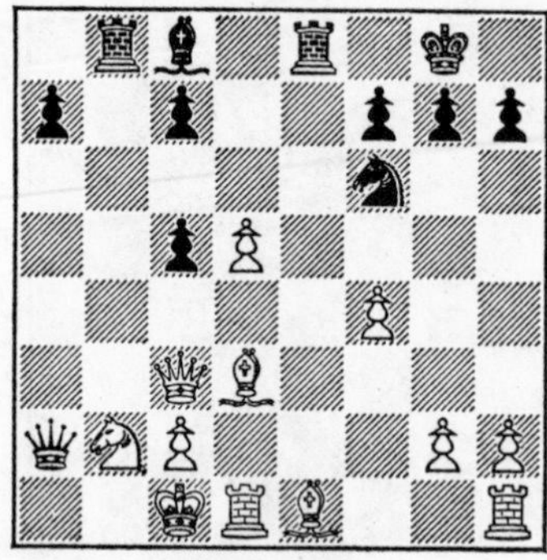

WHITE

Black moves

249. White wins a piece.
250. Another dramatic example of Pawn promotion. Black's defenses break down.
251. Another example of Pillsbury's splendid blindfold play.
252. Black cuts off the flight of White's King.

253

BLACK

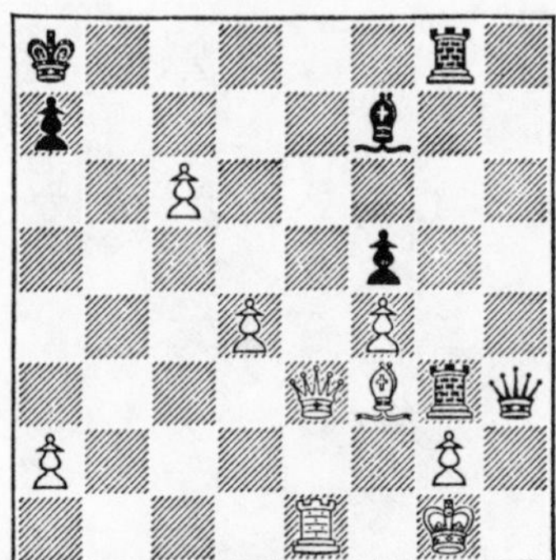

WHITE

White moves

254

BLACK

WHITE

Black moves

255

BLACK

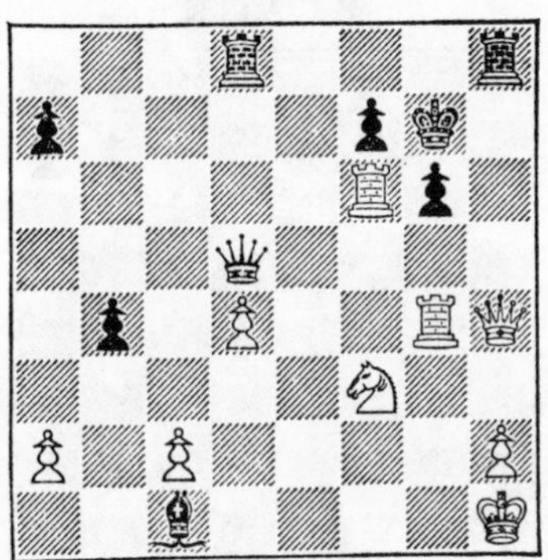

WHITE

White moves

256

BLACK

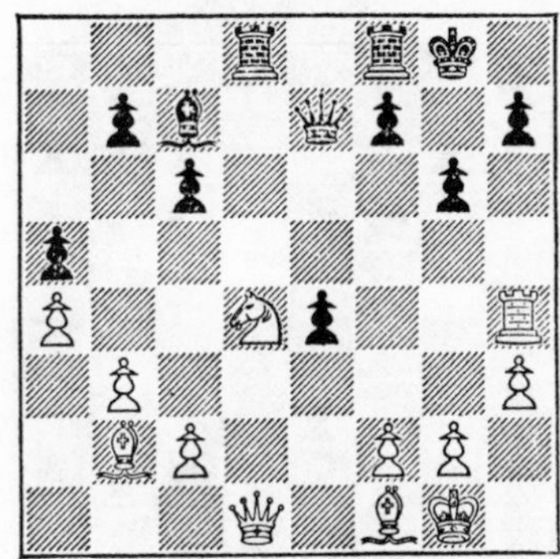

WHITE

White moves

253. Another striking example of Pawn promotion.

254. White's Queen is insecure. How can Black prove this?

255. How does White save everything?

256. White utilizes the long diagonal in striking fashion.

257

BLACK

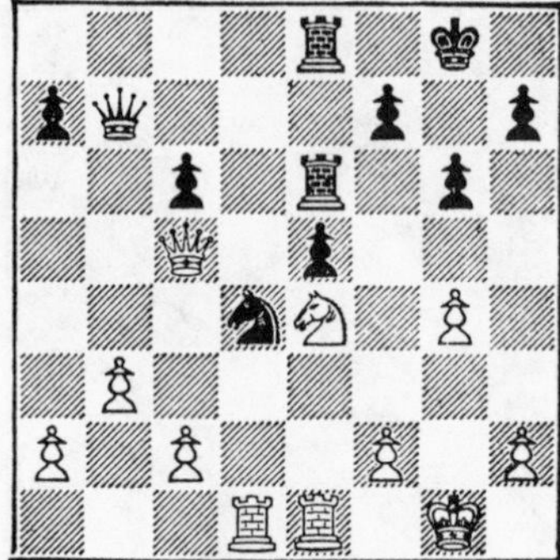

WHITE
White moves

258

BLACK

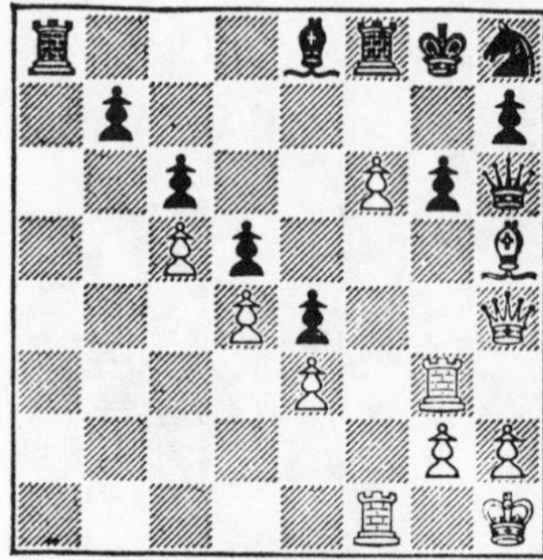

WHITE
White moves

259

BLACK

WHITE
White moves

260

BLACK

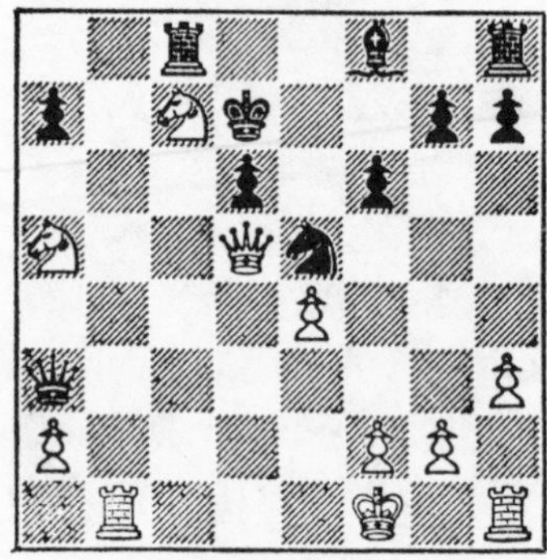

WHITE
White moves

257. Pillsbury wins quickly.
258. A brilliant combination from one of Janowski's odds-games.
259. Black's attack is easily repulsed.
260. The winning method requires precision.

THIRTEENTH QUIZ

241. A neat sacrifice of the Queen with an even neater sequel: *1* Q×P *ch!* K×Q; *2* R–R5 *ch,* K–Kt1; *3* Kt–Kt6! and mate follows.

242. A familiar theme, expertly handled by Rubinstein: *1* R×Kt! B×R; *2* Kt–B6 *ch,* K–B1; *3* Kt–Q5! winning the Queen.

243. White's stranglehold on the KKt file decides quickly: *1* Q–K2! Q–R2; *2* R×Kt! P×R; *3* R–Kt5 followed by R–R5 winning the Queen.

244. Black threatens mate, but he is forestalled by *1* Q×P *ch!!* K×Q; *2* B–R3 *ch,* K–B5; *3* B–Kt5 *ch,* K×P; *4* QR–B1 *mate!*

245. White has a charming mating combination with *1* Q×P *ch!* K×Q; *2* B–B5 *ch,* K–Kt4 (if 2 . . . K–R4; 3 P–Kt4 *ch,* Kt×P; 4 R–R3 *ch,* K–Kt4; 5 Kt–K4 mate or 3 . . . K–Kt4; 4 B–K3 *ch,* K–R5; 5 B–B2 *ch,* K–Kt4; 6 P–R4 mate); *3* B–K3 *ch,* K–R4; *4* P–Kt4 *ch,* K–R5; *5* B–B2 *ch,* K–Kt4; *6* P–R4 *mate.*

246. Still another immolation of the White Queen: *1* Q–R5 ch! P×Q; *2* Kt–B5 *mate!*

247. White wins in fine style with *1* R×B! P×R (if 1 . . . R×B; 2 R–B5 *ch,* R–B2; 3 Q×R *ch,* Q×Q; 4 R×Q *ch,* K×R; 5 P–R6); *2* P–QR6! P×P (if 2 . . . Q×B; 3 Q×Q, R×Q; 4 P–R7!); *3* Q×RP *ch* winning Black's Queen.

248. Black has a very pretty win, the main line being *1*... Q–B4 *ch; 2* K–R1, Q–B5! *3* K–Kt1, Q–Q5 *ch! 4* K–R1, Q–K5! *5* Q–QB1, Q–Q6! *6* K–Kt1, Q–Q5 *ch! 7* K–R1, Q–Q7! winning the Rook.

249. White wins a piece: *1* P–B5! B–K2 (or 1 . . . P×P;

2 P×P, B–K2; 3 B×Kt); 2 P–Q5! threatening both B×Kt and P–Q6.

250. Black has abandoned his first rank to its fate: *1* R–K8 *ch!* Kt×R; *2* Q–B3 *ch,* Kt–Kt2; *3* Q×Kt *ch!* (removes the blockader), K×Q; *4* P–R8(Q) *ch,* etc.

251. One of Pillsbury's blindfold finishes: *1* Q–K5 (or 1 Q–KB4), Q–B1; *2* Q–Q6! followed by R–Kt8 *ch!*

252. Black concludes forcefully with *1* . . . R–K7!! 2 B×R, Kt–K5 and mate is unavoidable.

253. White (Mieses) wins with *1* Q–K8 *ch!* R×Q; *2* R×R *ch,* B×R; *3* P–B7 *ch,* R×B; *4* P–B8(Q) *mate.*

254. The pretty move *1* . . . Kt×RP!! leaves White helpless, for if *2* Q–K2, Kt×P *ch!* *3* Q×Kt, Q×Kt *ch!* *4* K×Q, R–R5 *mate.*

255. In this position, so dangerous for both players, White wins with *1* R(6)×KtP *ch!* P×R; *2* Q–K7 *ch,* Q–B2; *3* R×P *ch!* K×R; *4* Kt–K5 *ch,* etc.

256. This is surely one of the prettiest combinations on record: *1* Kt–B5!! Q×R; *2* Q–R5!! and Black resigns.

257. White wins nicely with *1* R×Kt! P×R; *2* Kt–B6 *ch,* K–R1 (if 2 . . . K–Kt2; 3 Kt×R *ch*); *3* R×R! and Black is helpless.

258. White (Janowski) giving Knight odds, brings off a magnificent finish: *1* B×P! Q×Q; *2* B–B7 *ch!!* K×B; *3* R–Kt7 *ch,* K–K3; *4* R–K7 *mate.*

259. Black lacks adequate defensive resources: *1* Q–R5, P–KR3; *2* P–B6, Kt×R; *3* Q–Kt6! P×Q; *4* Kt–K7 *ch,* K–R1; *5* Kt×P *mate.*

260. White has various ways of winning, the quickest being *1* Q–K6 *ch,* K×Kt; *2* R–Kt7 *ch,* K–Q1; *3* Kt–B6 *ch!* and mate in two.

FOURTEENTH QUIZ

261

BLACK

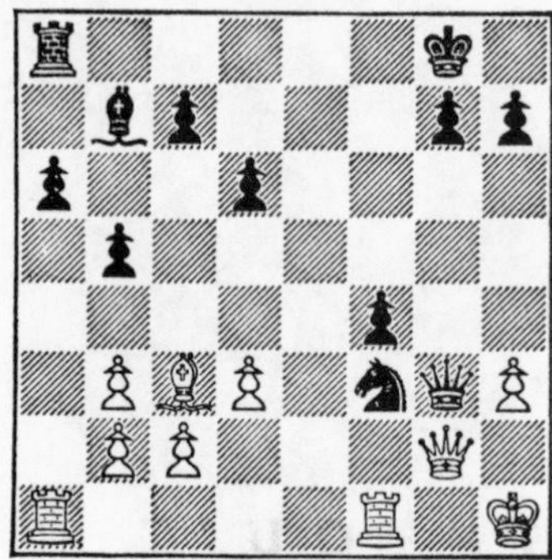

WHITE
Black moves

262

BLACK

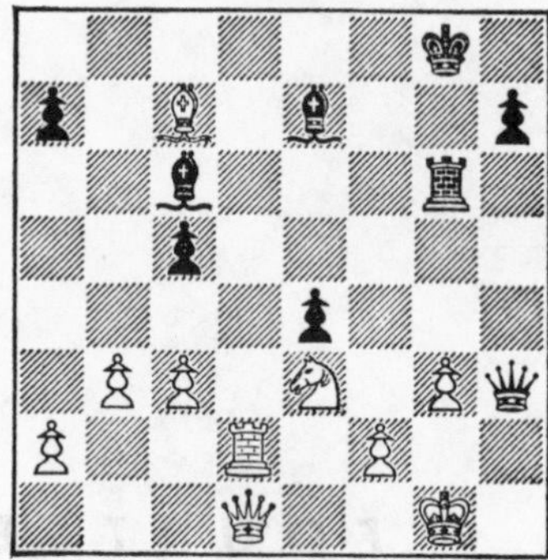

WHITE
Black moves

263

BLACK

WHITE
White moves

264

BLACK

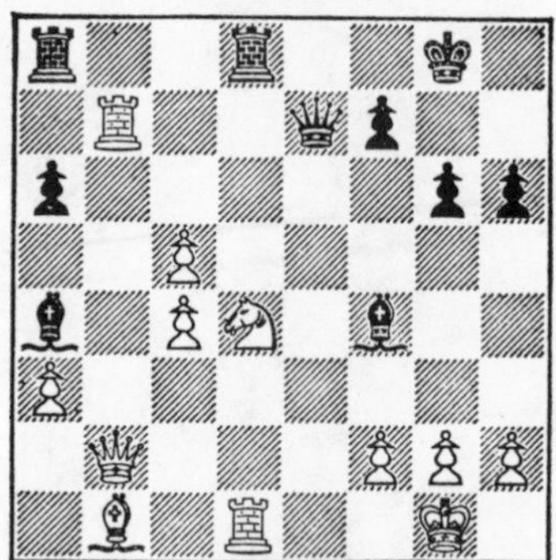

WHITE
Black moves

261. The presence of White's King and Queen on the same diagonal is unhealthy.

262. Black wins a piece.

263. White wins elegantly.

264. Should Black withdraw the Queen from attack, or does he have some other resource?

265

BLACK

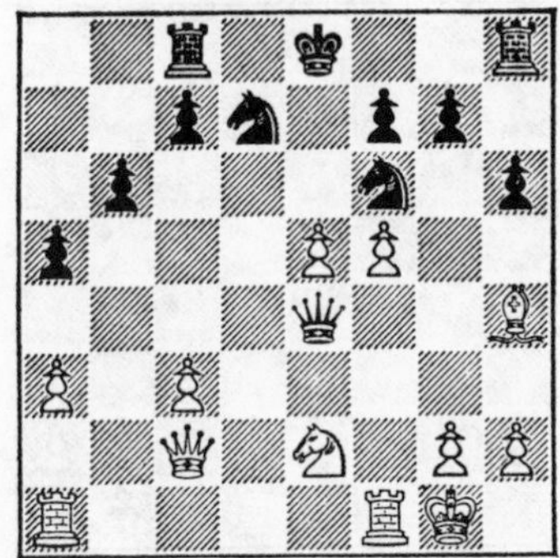

WHITE

White moves

266

BLACK

WHITE

Black moves

267

BLACK

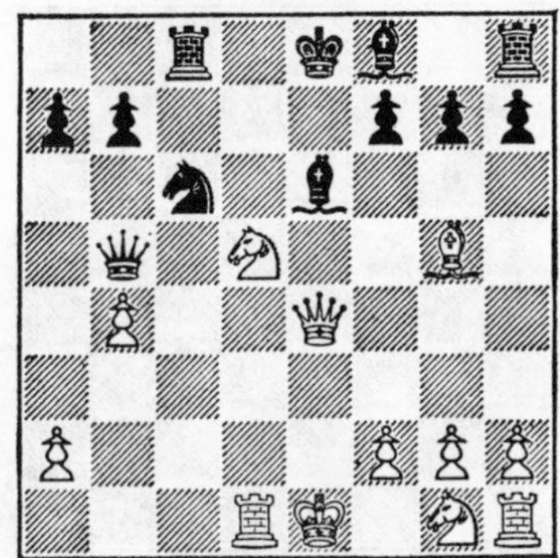

WHITE

White moves

268

BLACK

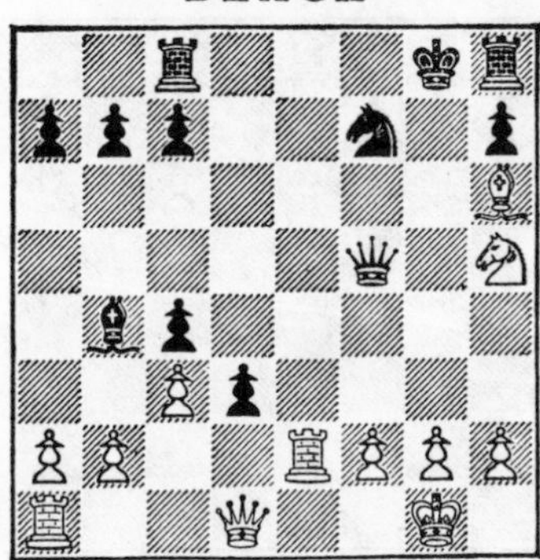

WHITE

White moves

265. Capablanca is punished for not having castled.

266. Black's attack strikes home first.

267. White has a pretty forced mate.

268. An inspired combination wins for White.

269

BLACK

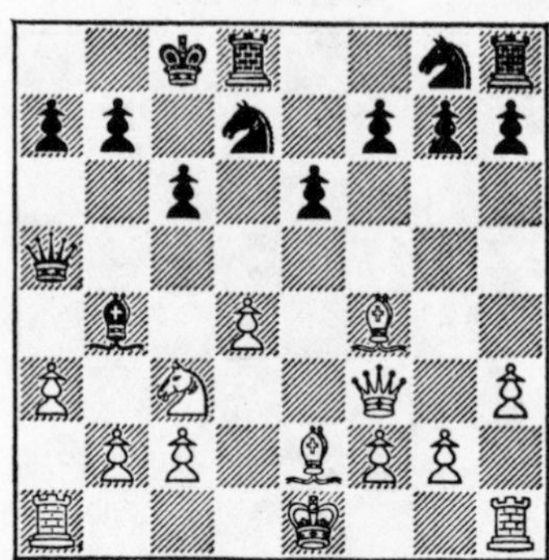

WHITE
White moves

270

BLACK

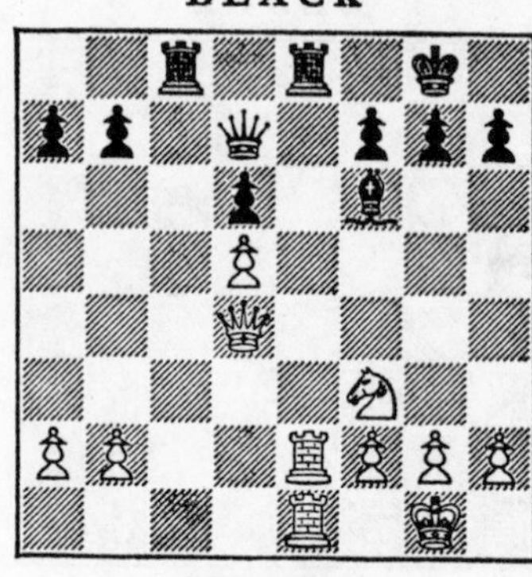

WHITE
White moves

271

BLACK

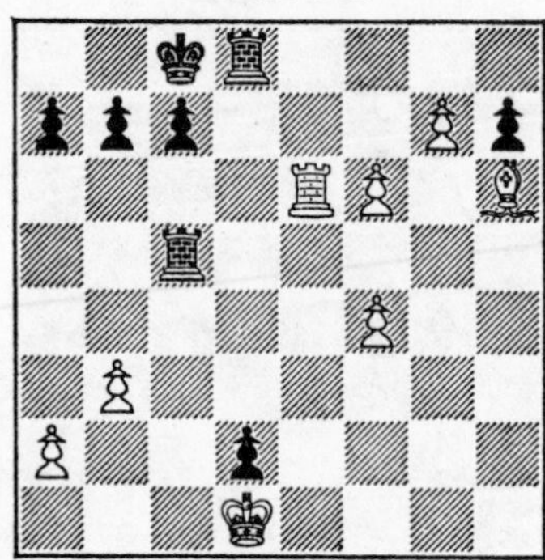

WHITE
White moves

272

BLACK

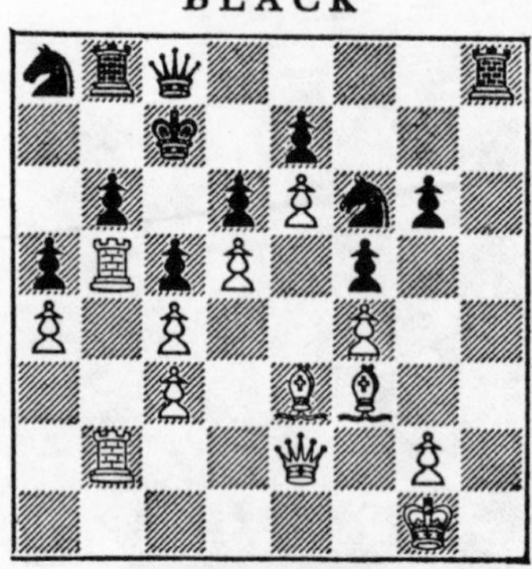

WHITE
White moves

269. A classic win by Canal.
270. White brings off one of the greatest combinations on record.
271. Torre resigned in this position.
272. How can White make progress?

273

BLACK

WHITE
Black moves

274

BLACK

WHITE
White moves

275

BLACK

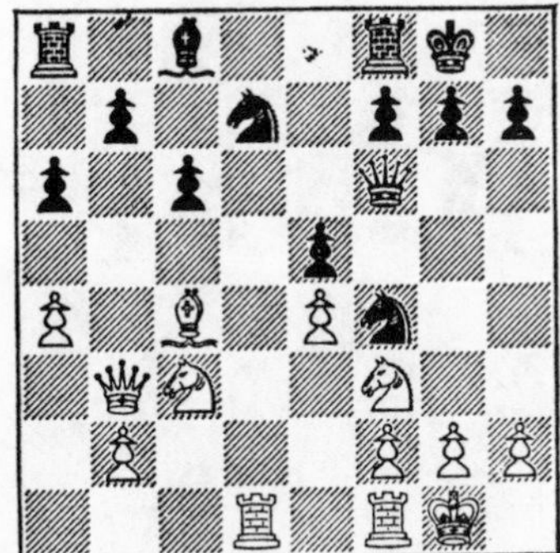

WHITE
Black moves

276

BLACK

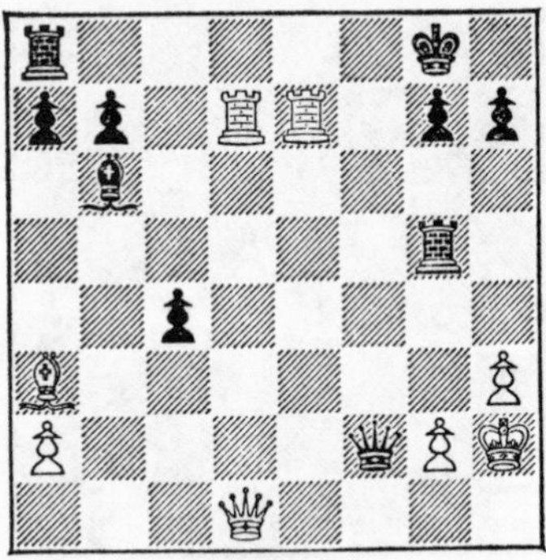

WHITE
White moves

273. Black has a magnificent position. The strongest attack is hard to find.

274. White wins by a subtle maneuver.

275. White's virtually undefended King-side is taken by storm.

276. Again the united Rooks show their power.

277

BLACK

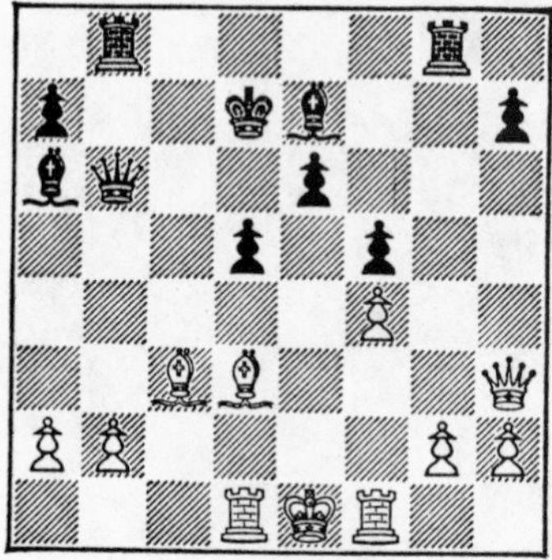

WHITE

Black moves

278

BLACK

WHITE

White moves

279

BLACK

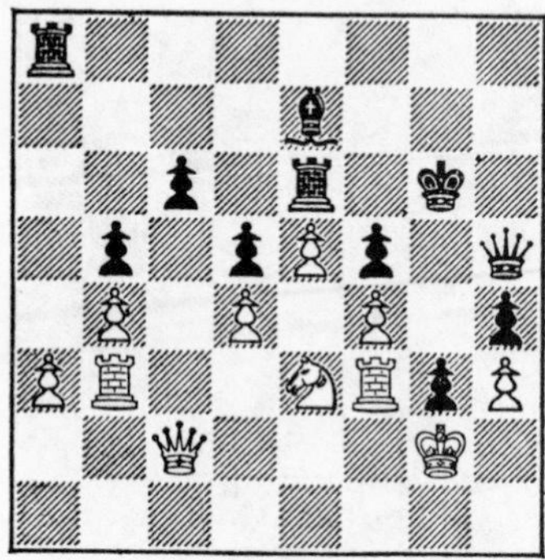

WHITE

White moves

280

BLACK

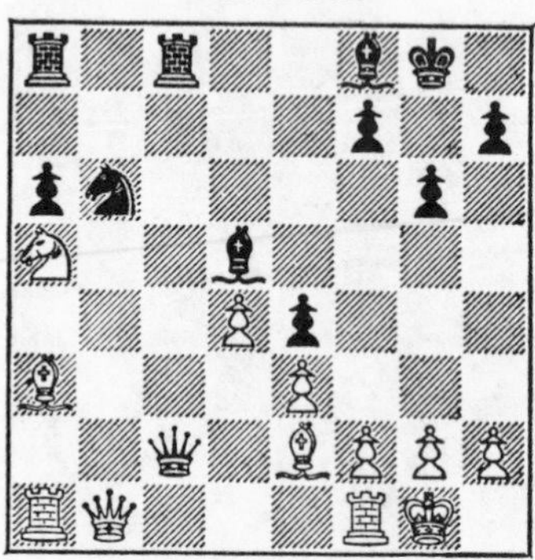

WHITE

Black moves

277. Mieses wins with one of the most beautiful moves ever played.

278. White wins by vigorous play.

279. White breaks through in an apparently blockaded position.

280. Botvinnik works out a clever combination.

FOURTEENTH QUIZ

261. Black has a winning combination with a surprising first move: *1* . . . Kt–Q5! *2* Q×B, Q×P *ch; 3* K–Kt1, Kt–K7 *ch; 4* K–B2, Q–K6 *ch* and mate in two more moves.

262. There is a curious win by *1* . . . R–R3; *2* Q–Kt4 *ch,* Q×Q; *3* Kt×Q, R–R8 *ch! 4* K×R, P–K6 *ch; 5* K–Kt1, P×R; *6* Kt–K3, B–B6, etc.

263. White wins in amusing fashion with *1* Q–Kt8 *ch!* K×Q; *2* Kt–K7 *ch,* K–B1; *3* either Kt–Kt6 *ch,* P×Kt; *4* Kt×P *mate.*

264. Instead of moving his menaced Queen, Black leaves his opponent helpless with *1* . . . R×Kt!!

265. White calmly leaves his Queen en prise and plays *1* P×Kt!! Q×Q (after 1 . . . Q×B; 2 P×P, KR–Kt1; 3 P–B6! White has an easy win); *2* P×P, KR–Kt1; *3* Kt–Q4! Q–K5 (if 3 . . . Q×P; 4 either R–K1 *ch,* Kt–K4; 5 R×Kt *ch,* K–Q2; 6 R–K7 *ch,* K–Q3; 7 Kt–Kt5 *ch*); *4* QR–K1, Kt–B4; *5* R×Q *ch,* Kt×R; *6* R–K1, etc.

266. The KR file is put to good use: *1* . . . R×P *ch!* *2* B×R, Kt–Kt6 *ch! 3* B×Kt, Q–R1 *ch; 4* B–R2, Q×B *ch!* *5* K×Q, R–R1 *ch* and mate next move.

267. An adaptation of a famous Morphy combination: *1* Kt–B7 *ch!* R×Kt; *2* Q×Kt *ch!* and wins.

268. White's important pieces are ruthlessly disposed of in order to mate with the minor pieces: *1* R–K8 *ch!* R×R; *2* Q–Kt4 *ch!* Q×Q; *3* Kt–B6 *mate.*

269. White gladly parts with both Rooks—for a consideration: *1* P×B! Q×R *ch; 2* K–Q2, Q×R; *3* Q×P *ch!* P×Q; *4* B–R6 *mate.*

270. White wins by a series of magnificent forcing moves: *1* Q–KKt4! Q–Kt4; *2* Q–QB4! Q–Q2; *3* Q–B7!!

Q—Kt4; *4* P—QR4! Q×RP; *5* R—K4!! Q—Kt4; *6* Q×KtP! and Black resigns. A case of inadequately protected first rank.

271. White resigned at this point, although he could have won with *1* R—Q6!! R×R (if 1 ... P×R; 2 P—B7, etc.); *2* P—Kt8(Q) *ch*, K—Q2; *3* Q—B7 *ch*, K—B3; *4* Q—K8 *ch*, K—Kt3; *5* Q—K3! and wins.

272. The position is so barricaded that there seems to be no way for White to break through. But he finds a way: *1* B×P! QP×B; *2* R×P *ch!* P×R; *3* Q—K5 *ch* and wins.

273. Black wins with a beautiful combination: *1* . . . Kt—Kt6 *ch!* *2* P×Kt (or 2 Q×Kt, R×Q; 3 P×R, Q—K7), Q—R5 *ch!* *3* P×Q, R—R6 *mate!*

274. An extraordinary conclusion for over the board play: *1* R—QKt6! K×R (if 1 . . . R×R? 2 Kt×P mate!); *2* K×R with an easy win.

275. Playing with his customary energy, Black (Naidorf) wins with *1* . . . Kt×KtP! *2* K×Kt, Kt—B4! *3* Q—B2, B—R6 *ch!* *4* K×B, Q×Kt *ch; 5* K—R4, P—Kt4 *ch!* *6* K×P, K—R1, etc.

276. A charming winning maneuver: *1* Q—Q5 *ch!* K—R1 (if 1 . . . R×Q White mates in two); *2* R—Q8 *ch!* R×R; *3* Q×R *ch!* B×Q; *4* R—K8 *ch* and mate next move. Again the inadequately protected first rank!

277. Black (Mieses) wins the Queen with an exquisite combination: *1* . . . R—Kt6!! *2* Q×R, B—R5!

278. *1* B—B7 *ch*, K—K2; *2* Q×Kt *ch!!* K×Q; *3* Kt—Q5 *ch*, K—K4; *4* Kt—B3 *ch*, K×P; *5* Kt—B3 *mate!*

279. White smashes up the barricaded position with *1* Kt×BP!! Q×Kt; *2* R×P *ch!* P×R; *3* R×P *ch*, etc.

280. Botvinnik starts a series of simple exchanges with an unexpected sting: *1* . . . B×B; *2* R×B, Q×B; *3* Q×Kt, QR—Kt1; *4* Q—Q6, Q×R *ch!* forcing mate!

FIFTEENTH QUIZ

281

BLACK

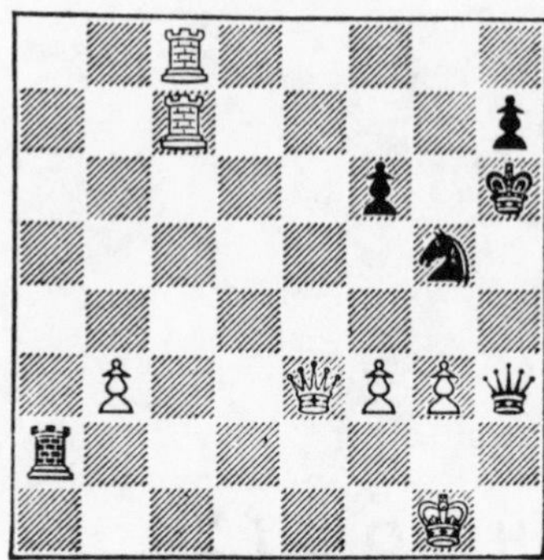

WHITE
White moves

282

BLACK

WHITE
White moves

283

BLACK

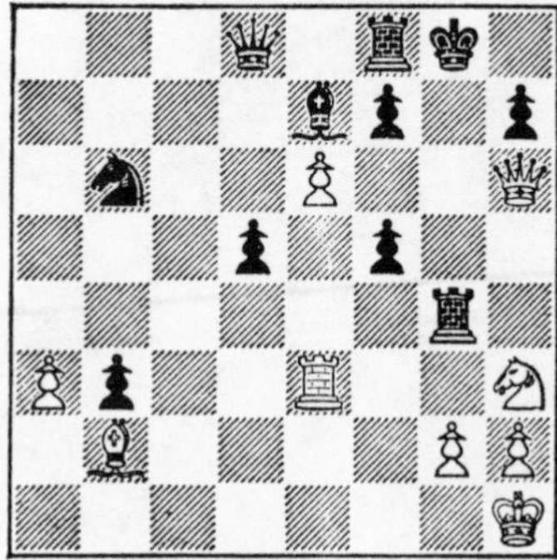

WHITE
White moves

284

BLACK

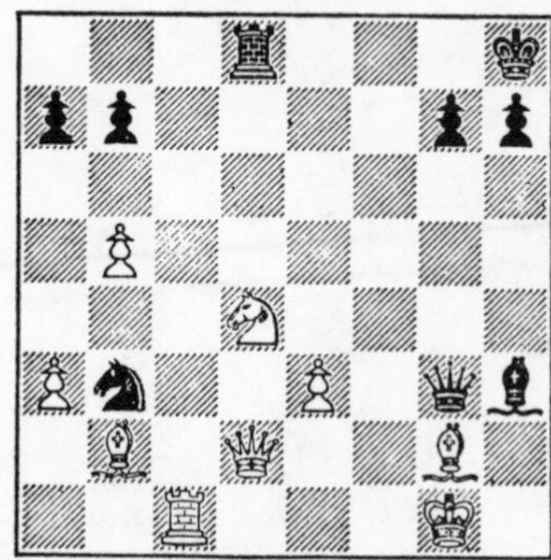

WHITE
White moves

281. Who wins?

282. Bondarevsky has a combination with an unexpected sting. An echo of a problem theme.

283. How does White prove the soundness of his previous sacrifice?

284. White repulses the attack elegantly.

285

BLACK

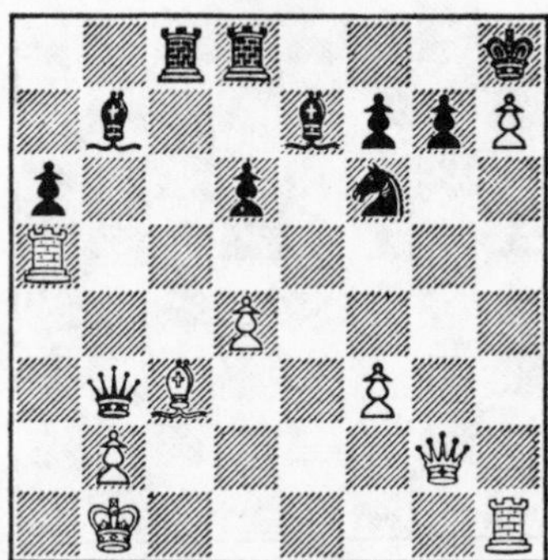

WHITE

White moves

286

BLACK

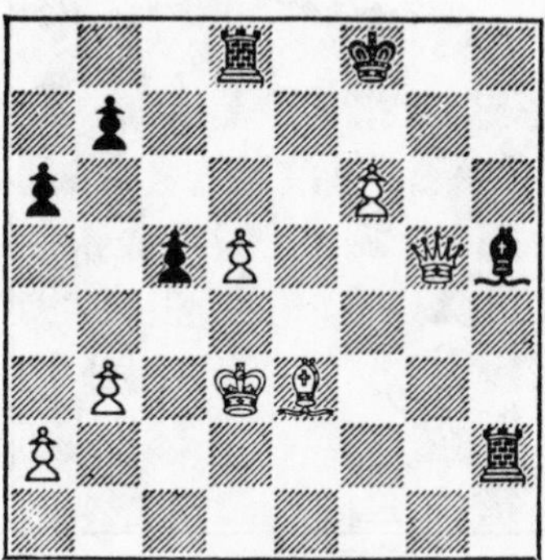

WHITE

Black moves

287

BLACK

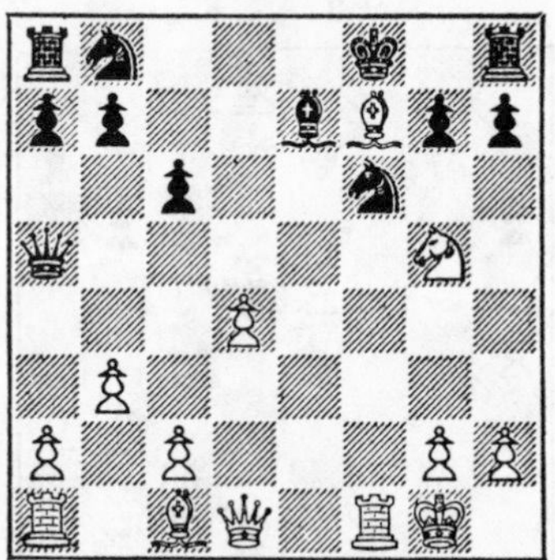

WHITE

White moves

288

BLACK

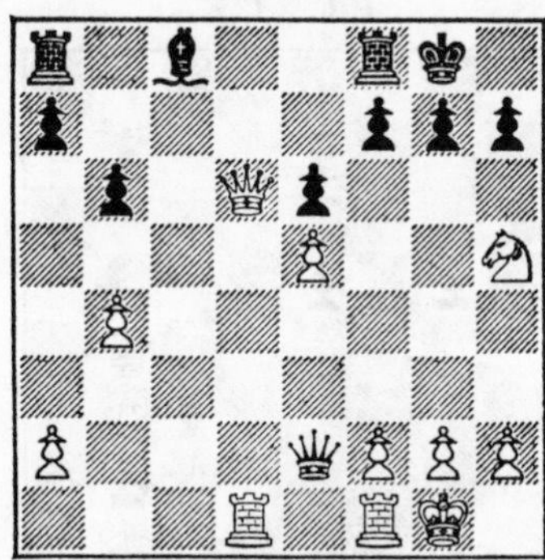

WHITE

White moves

285. A diabolically clever utilization of Pawn promotion.

286. Can Black save the game?

287. White's next move decides at once.

288. White can hardly be blamed for missing this subtle forced win.

289

BLACK

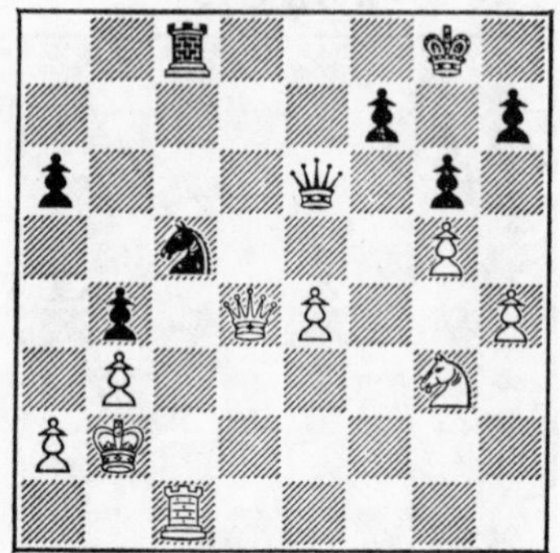

WHITE

Black moves

290

BLACK

WHITE

Black moves

291

BLACK

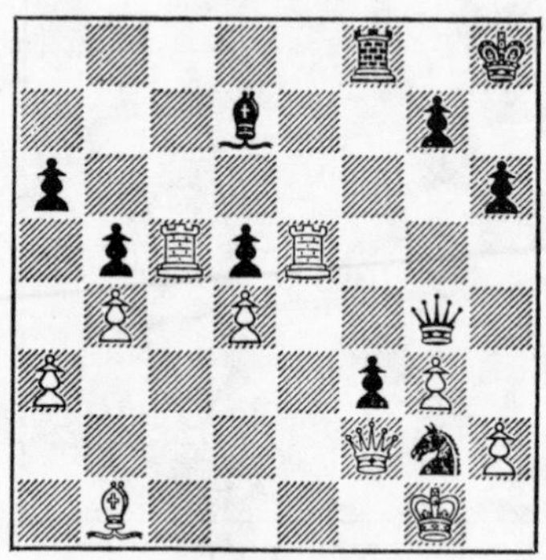

WHITE

White moves

292

BLACK

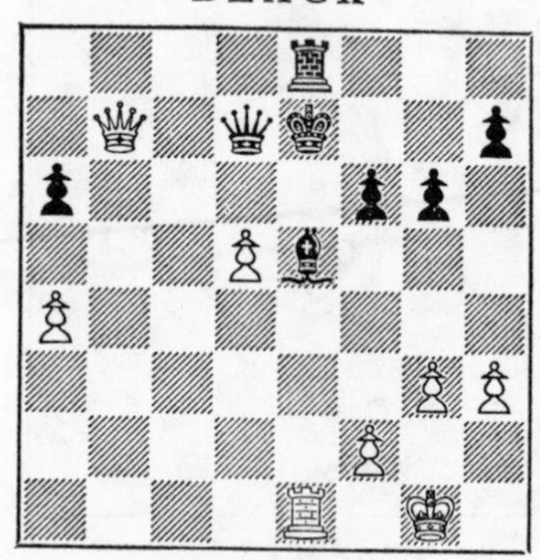

WHITE

White moves

289. Black win prettily.
290. A famous brilliancy-prize win.
291. White wins a piece.
292. Capablanca wins the Queen.

293

BLACK

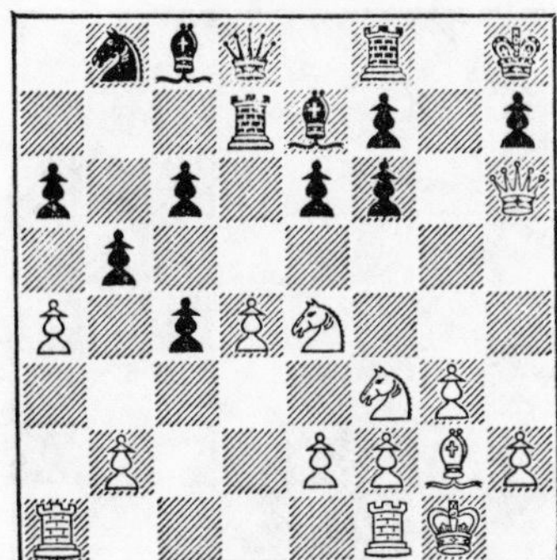

WHITE

White moves

294

BLACK

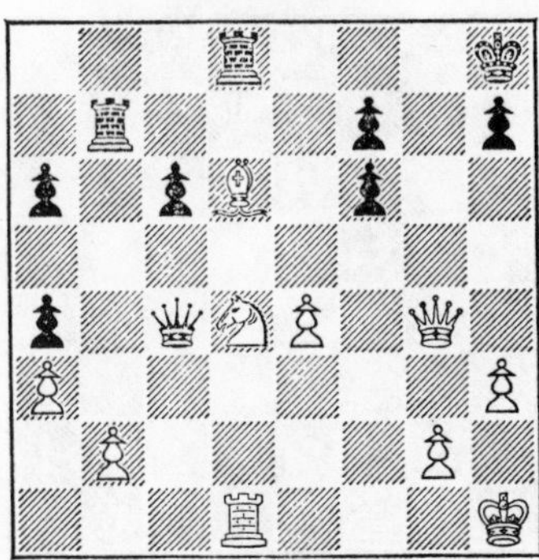

WHITE

White moves

295

BLACK

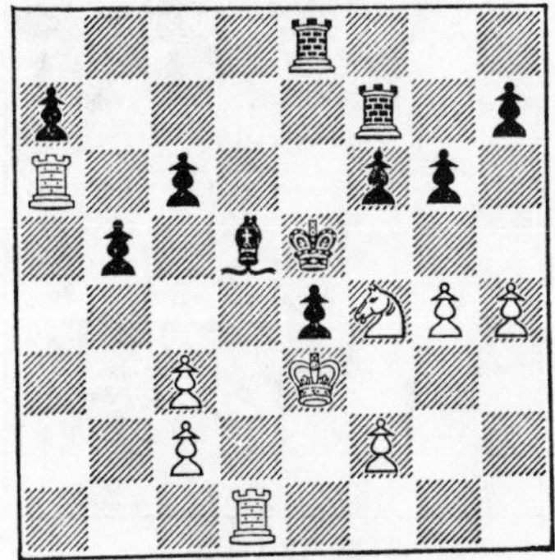

WHITE

White moves

296

BLACK

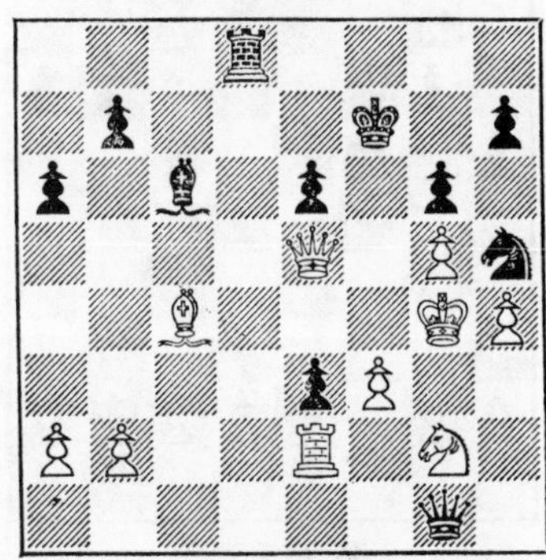

WHITE

Black moves

293. White wins in very brilliant style.

294. The first move is obvious . . .

295. A remarkably fine combination.

296. A masterly combination by Stahlberg.

297

BLACK

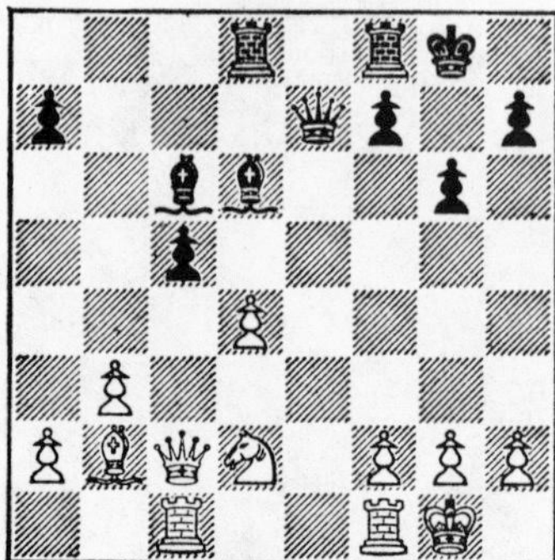

WHITE

Black moves

298

BLACK

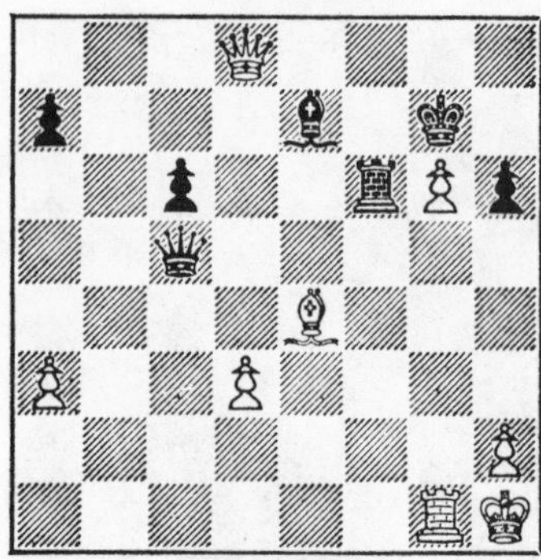

WHITE

White moves

299

BLACK

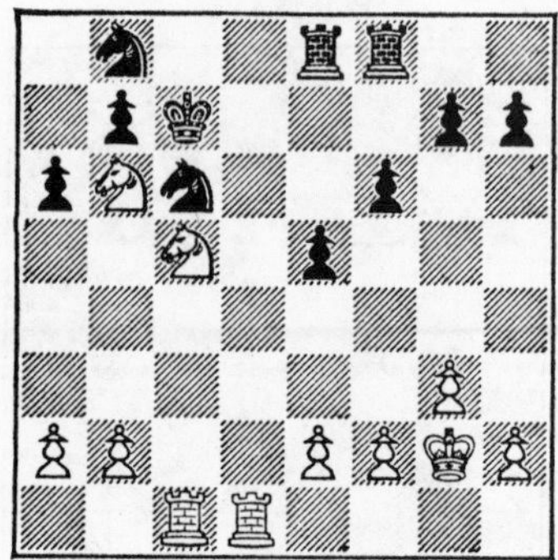

WHITE

White moves

300

BLACK

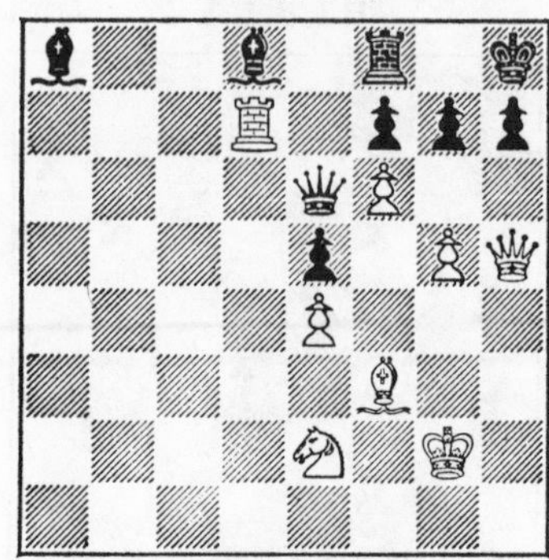

WHITE

White moves

297. One of the great combinations.

298. Pawn promotion is still effective! White smashes all obstacles vigorously.

299. The Knights cooperate with comical effectiveness.

300. White's attack is carried through superbly.

FIFTEENTH QUIZ

281. A superb combination: *1* R×P *ch!!* K×R; *2* Q—K7 *ch,* K—Kt3; *3* R—Kt8 *ch,* K—B4; *4* R×Kt *ch!* K×R; *5* Q—Kt7 *ch,* K—B4; *6* Q—Q7 *ch* winning the Queen.

282. White deflects Black's Knight from the defense: *1* R—R8 *ch,* K—B2; *2* B—K8 *ch!!* Kt×B; *3* K—Kt5 and Black cannot stop mate.

283. White has sacrificed a piece for an attack which he concludes successfully with *1* Kt—Kt5!! R×Kt; *2* R—R3.

284. White's position seems hopeless, but he extricates himself with the winning move *1* Kt—B5!! Again the inadequately protected last rank tells the story.

285. White puts the KRP to good use: *1* Q×P *ch!* K×Q; *2* P—R8(Q) *ch!* R×Q; *3* R—Kt5 *ch,* K—B1; *4* R×R *ch* and mate next move.

286. Black simplifies cleverly with *1* . . . R×P *ch!* *2* Q×R, B—Kt3 *ch; 3* Q—K4, B×Q *ch,* etc.

287. Black is in a bad way, and *1* Q—R5! finishes him off directly.

288. White missed the pretty win *1* Kt—B6 *ch!!* P×Kt; *2* P×P and Black cannot guard against the double threat of Q×R *ch* and Q—Kt3 *ch.*

289. Black wins with the surprise move *1* . . . Q—K4!

290. Another "immortal": *1* . . . Kt—K7 *ch!* *2* R×Kt, R—B8 *ch!* *3* K×R, Q—R8 *ch;* 4 K—B2, Kt—Kt5 *mate.*

291. White begins a sly attack against Black's inadequately protected first rank with *1* P—R3!! Black must capture the RP. Then comes *2* Q×P!! R×Q (if the Rook moves away, White captures the Knight or plays Q—Q3); *3* R—B8 *ch!* B×R; *4* R—K8 *ch* and mate follows.

292. White has sacrificed a piece to win by means of a series of perfectly timed moves: *1* P–Q6 *ch!* K–K3 (1 . . . K×P loses the Queen, and if 1 . . . K–Q1; 2 Q–Kt6 *ch* wins); *2* Q–Kt3 *ch,* K–B4; *3* Q–Q3 *ch,* K–Kt4 (if 3 . . . K–K3; 4 Q–B4 *ch,* K–B4; 5 Q–Kt4 mate); *4* Q–K3 *ch,* K–B4 (if 4 . . . K–R4; 5 P–Kt4 *ch,* K–R5; 6 Q–R6 mate); *5* Q–K4 *ch,* K–K3 (or 5 . . . K–Kt4; 6 Q–R4 *ch,* K–B4; 7 Q–Kt4 mate); *6* Q–B4 *ch* and wins.

293. Black's precarious position is stormed with *1* Kt(3)–Kt5!! P×Kt; *2* Kt–B6!! B×Kt; *3* B–K4 and mate cannot be prevented!

294. The end comes with surprising suddenness: *1* Kt–B5, R–KKt1; *2* B–K5!!

295. A conclusion which seems to have come out of a problem: *1* R×B *ch!* P×R; *2* Kt–Q3 *ch!* P×Kt; *3* P–B4 *mate.*

296. Another unusual conclusion for over the board play: *1* . . . R–Q5 *ch!!* *2* Q×R, Q–R7! and White has no good move.

297. A famous combination: *1* . . . B×P *ch!!* *2* K×B, Q–R5 *ch;* *3* K–Kt1, B×P! *4* K×B, Q–Kt5 *ch;* *5* K–R1, R–Q4; *6* Q×P, R×Q and wins; or *4* P–B3, KR–K1; *5* Kt–K4, Q–R8 *ch;* *6* K–B2, B×R, etc.

298. Black's King is a very poor blockader: *1* Q–R8 *ch!* K×Q; *2* P–Kt7 *ch,* K–Kt1; *3* B–R7 *ch!* etc.

299. The quiet move *1* Kt(5)–R4!! leaves Black helpless, for instance *1* . . . R–Q1; *2* Kt–R8 *ch,* K–B1; *3* Kt(4)–Kt6 *mate.*

300. Black is crushed by *1* P–Kt6! P–R3; *2* Q×P *ch!* P×Q; *3* P–Kt7 *ch,* K–Kt1; *4* P×R(Q) *ch,* K×Q; *5* R×B *ch* and wins.